WITH EYES WIDE OPEN

a workbook
for parents adopting
international children

Margi Miller, M.A.
Nancy Ward, M.A., LICSW

1605 Eustis Street
St. Paul, MN 55108
651-646-6393 or 800-952-9302
www.childrenshomeadopt.org

With Eyes Wide Open
a workbook for parents adopting international children

Children's Home Society & Family Services
1605 Eustis Street
St. Paul, MN 55108
phone: 651-646-6393 or toll free 800-952-9302
fax: 651-646-0436
web: www.childrenshomeadopt.org
e-mail: welcome@chsfs.org

LN Press, Incorporated
4801 Folwell Drive
Minneapolis, MN 55406
Copyright 1996 by Children's Home Society of Minnesota

Notice of Rights

Notice of Liability

Acknowledgements
Cover photo by Kevin Horan/Chicago 1998

We wish to thank David Pilgrim, Julie Hessler and Maureen Evans for their untiring editing, and the staff of Children's Home Society & Family Services for their support.

Photographs courtesy of Corel Corporation and CHSFS adoptive families

Revised: March 2005
Also available in CD format

ISBN 0-9621729-4-4

Inside

Dear Adoptive Parent,

You have been asked to use this workbook to prepare for one of the most life-challenging and rewarding experiences you will ever have: taking a child into your heart and your life to be a part of you forever.

More specifically, this workbook is for parents about to adopt an international child with life experiences, the words we use to describe a child 12 months old or older who is already searching or attempting to attach to a parent figure who can meet her/his needs, who has already experienced pain and hopefully its relief, who recognizes a repeated pattern of distinct sounds (voices, words, verbal, and non-verbal communications from a caregiver), who is learning his/her own body and what it can or cannot do or achieve, and who recognizes friend or foe.

Because you will have missed the first year or more of your future child's life, we ask you to come with us on the adventure of reconstructing that child's experiences. The methodology, in brief, will ask you to imagine your child's life, research it, role play, answer questions, and discuss how you might parent this child. Although the techniques of imagining and role playing are difficult for many people, we ask that you attempt them, either in a group or privately, and recognize and allow yourselves to feel the emotions they might evoke: fear, panic, longing, disgust and tenderness.

This workbook may raise questions for which you do not have answers or issues that seem perplexing. Use the difficult exercises as a means to work with your adoption agency or parent group, or consult the resource chapter at the end of the workbook to find books and tapes to help you.

We take our inspiration and learning from adoptive parents who have been participants at Children's Home Society & Family Services workshops where we do these exercises together. They work for many parents, and we hope they will serve your needs. We welcome your suggestions.

Margi Miller and Nancy Ward
Children's Home Society & Family Services
First Printing, August 1996
Revised Edition, March 2005

1

The Image of Our Child

Yes, this exercise may be the hardest of all. It asks you to draw a picture of your future child. You may already have a snapshot or video, or perhaps just a picture in your mind of what your child will look like. But take the time here to draw (okay, you can take out the page when you are done and hide it!) What is important is the doing.

As you draw the face, fingers, toes, go ahead and let yourself touch them as you will touch your child. If you feel timid now, you will feel timid then, so practice. Make the eyes you draw look right at you and ask you for something. The clothes you put on your child will be ones you have chosen. This should be fun. Remember to include the details that will set your child apart from all the others—buttons, jewelry, colorful badges, socks that make a statement. This exercise asks you to choose an age, the race of your child, the gender. It is not a permanent decision, just an exercise.

Questions

Answering or discussing questions after an exercise can be as important or even more important than the exercise itself. Please read through the questions below. Then, decide on your best style of reflection: small or large group discussion, journaling, talking with your partner, or personal quiet time.

What part of this drawing was the most poignant for you?

_____

_____

Does this tell you something about how you relate/will relate to your child?

_____

_____

Is it what you want? What your spouse/family will also want?

_____

_____

What part did you spend the most time on? Why? What does this tell you?

_____

_____

_____

What emotions did this exercise evoke?

_____

_____

_____

_____

2

· · · · · · · · · · · · · ·

Adoption Losses and Gains

When parents give birth to children seldom do the following questions arise:

Will this child ever be taken away or taken back? Will this child "fit" in our family?

But adoptive parents sometimes do face these questions, as well as others unique to adoption:

How would our lives have been different if this were our birth

child? Will I ever reject this child? Will this child grow to hate me because of the adoption? Will he/she want to "go back"? Will I raise this child differently because he/she is not my birth child?

How will I feel the first time this child says "My birth mother wouldn't treat me as badly as you do."? How about "I hate you. You're not my real mother."?

Experiences of loss

Before parents adopt, these questions are usually not considered or are suppressed. Yet they are real questions for many, many adoptive parents after the adoption, which makes it likely that you too will confront them.

It is said that parents who have chosen to adopt gain something wonderful and lose something great. They gain a child, make their family international, fulfill a dream and create a dynamic of yet another type of love: parental love for a child. They lose also. They may lose the making of a child together, they may lose the months of pregnancy with all its emotions and care by others. In adoption, they lose being the American normative family, the expected typical family. They lose the possibility of a child who resembles them, carries their talents in the genes, and carries on the family genes to a new generation.

They may even subconsciously reject or over-protect their adopted child because of their own past experiences.

Examples:
- Parents who have experienced miscarriages may steer their child away from any adventuresome activity because they might "lose" him.
- Parents who feel self-conscious that their adopted child is not really "theirs" may feel they cannot discipline their child.
- Parents who have waited long to be parents might make up for lost time by giving their adopted child every toy and experience.

Even as you read and perhaps resist thinking that any of these losses apply to you, it might be good to read them over again. Permit yourself to wonder about them. Why? So that you will recognize them when and if they occur later. In later chapters we will learn about the losses children often feel and cannot express in words. We'll explore ways to help them.

Exercise

This exercise, based on other losses in life, helps to ask the questions about losses and gains in adoption:

Write here a talent you always wished you had:

_____

_____

_____

Name here a few luxuries you would love to have in your present house:

_____

_____

_____

What are some of life's lessons you wish you had learned better in high school or college?

_____

_____

_____

Write here something for which you had to wait for a very long time:

_____

_____

_____

Write here about a profession you didn't pursue but secretly wished you could have:

_____

_____

_____

What are a few places you wish you would have visited?

_____

_____

_____

Questions

1. As you wrote things you wished for but knew might never come true, what feelings were you aware of?

    _____

    _____

    _____

    _____

2.	What relation do you see between these feelings and your experience of adoption?

_____

_____

_____

_____

_____

_____

_____

_____

3.	You read earlier the list of losses for adoptive parents. List here what might be the losses for your child.

_____

_____

_____

_____

_____

_____

_____

_____

4.	What will your future adopted child gain by joining your family?

_____

_____

_____

_____

_____

_____

_____

_____

_____

_____

5. Most people would agree that "The last person in the world who would ever abandon or reject me would be my mother." Yet this is exactly what many adopted children have experienced. Comment on how this might affect your future parenting.

_____
_____
_____
_____
_____

6. A child may feel loss, grief, and sadness, but may show these feelings in opposite ways, such as cover-ups, denial, anger, false happiness, and control. Give an example of what you might say or ask a child to help her understand why she has these feelings.

_____
_____
_____
_____
_____

Discussion

With your group or spouse, try to elaborate on each of these possible losses for your adopted child as she leaves her country to come to you:

*   language
*   familiar sounds
*   being in a group
*   friends
*   special tastes and smells
*   a sense of place
*   being held a certain way
*   the feel of his/her own crib or bed
*   what else?

To put adoption losses in perspective, consider that all children grow up with other losses in life. Try to continue and compare this list:

- not being athletic/handsome/thin/healthy
- having a disability or a parent/sibling with a disability
- _____
- _____
- _____
- _____

Thinking ahead to when your adopted child marries and/or becomes a parent, will she fear that she, too, will not be able to parent? Will she try to prove or disprove this by an early pregnancy?

_____
_____
_____
_____
_____
_____

What does the following mean to you?
"An adopted child tries to set up his world so there will be no more losses."

_____
_____
_____
_____
_____
_____

3
· · · · · · · · · · · · · · · ·

The Sounds of Early Life

Before children begin to understand or speak, they have logged thousands of hours of sounds. Although adoptive parents will not know what most of those sounds, words, or melodies might have been, it is useful to wonder about them and ask about them if possible.

This exercise asks you to imagine, recall, or research what happened to *you* as an infant, and then carries you on to the country of your future child.

My childhood experience

Imagine the house in which your birth parents lived and what songs, sounds, words, and sayings might have been spoken to you *in utero* or in the first years of life. If your parents are still alive, ask them. Note them here:

_____
_____
_____
_____
_____

While you are at it, ask what your first spoken word was and ask your parents to imitate your first babblings.

My child's experience

Now imagine the same for your future adopted child. Take a trip to a library or bookstore to borrow or buy a language tape or a music tape from that country, or try to get a recording of family life in that language. Then, in the dark, in your own bed, play the tape and let the sounds overtake you. If they becoming annoying, let that happen, too. That is actually part of the point of this exercise. Your child, if coming from a different country and language, may find the sounds of your sweet voice annoying, even frightening.

Assess your family, grandparents, friends. What kind of voices (loud, sharp, musical, etc.) will your child hear? Assess your home and community. What kind of sounds (traffic, birds, planes, pets, appliances) will your child hear? What sounds might never have been heard before by your child?

_____

_____

Is there any sound he/she might fear? Why?

_____

_____

_____

Learning My Child's Language

Try learning just a few words (even sounds) in the language of your child. Some parents think this is useless if their child is pre-verbal. Not so. Hearing the same sounds provides a wonderful transition for a child and creates a bond between new adoptive parents and their child. It is very worthwhile. So is singing songs together, especially children's songs. This is not language learning like a grammatical study or tips for travelers (although that will help). It is more like an imitation of sounds, where inflection and the quality of sound are very important.

In some adoption programs the international coordinators or agency staff can give you a videotape of your child in the orphanage or foster home. Use it to imitate your child's caretaker in voice, inflection, words, and gestures. To your child, this will be as comforting a transition as listening to your most favorite and nostalgic song during a period of sorrow or change in your life. Write here the words you think will be most useful or comforting to learn in your child's language.

_____

_____

_____

The Role of a Mentor

Try to find and make a friend in your town/city from the language and culture of your child. Making a new friend like this is not an easy task and you may feel like you are using the person rather than forming a friendship, or you may hesitate to share something so personal as your adoption dreams, but it is definitely worth it. What might you share?

_____
_____
_____
_____

If I only met once with this new person, how would I use the meeting to ask the person about my child's country? (Example: How are children in your country comforted when they cry?)

_____
_____

How and why might I want to share the celebration of our adoption later with this person?

_____
_____

What might be an example of overstepping a boundary with persons of this culture?

_____
_____
_____
_____
_____
_____
_____

Questions

1. What happens to you when you hear a familiar song from your childhood?

   _____

   _____

2. What are some family words or sayings that are unique to you? When does using these words or sayings become a positive or negative experience for you?

   _____

   _____

   _____

3. Do you look forward to teaching your child a new language with apprehension or with pleasure? Why?

   _____

   _____

   _____

4. What are some ways other than language that you can communicate with a child?

   _____

   _____

   _____

Exercise

With your spouse or friends, attempt an evening without any language communication. Include children of all ages if possible, and explain ahead of time that from the moment they arrive at your door you will not be able to use any words. (Explain ahead of time that you are practicing for your new family.) Or have everyone speak in gibberish. Another interesting twist to this evening would be to ask a family who speaks another language to come and not use English but only their other language, which you do not understand.

4

. . . .

Food and All It Means

If they can, most toddlers and pre-schoolers make up their own ceremonies or meanings about food. Watch them. You can see some of them gain a lot of power as they extend the meal time by dawdling or tossing or making a sensory game time of meals. They can use food to play out a myriad of rejections they might be feeling in their lives. Food time can be a loving time, an experimenting time, a fine motor skill tuning time, or a battle of the wills.

Food fills many needs

Observe the different styles of eating among your family and friends. Ask your siblings and parents for the highlights of your own saga with food, and jot them down here.

_____
_____
_____
_____
_____
_____
_____

What were rules regarding eating in your childhood family? You probably still react to or observe some of them.

_____
_____
_____
_____
_____

Next, note some of your own *current* food rituals by answering these questions:

1. How does food fill some of my/ our emotional needs?

    _____
    _____
    _____

2. What kinds of foods do you eat? When and where are they eaten? What purposes do these foods or drinks serve?

_____

_____

_____

_____

_____

_____

_____

3. What foods do you refuse to eat? Why?

_____

_____

_____

_____

4. Which of the above would we like to or not like to pass on to our children? What can we do now to make some behavioral changes that might prepare us for the future?

_____

_____

_____

_____

_____

_____

Experience different foods

For an intercultural experience, get a common recipe from your future child's country and prepare the food, whether it sounds appetizing to you or not. Eat it with these questions in mind.

What caused me to like or dislike this food?

Texture of the food_____

Color_____

Spices _____

Hot/Cold _____

Bland/Spicy _____

How much work in preparation _____

Ingredients _____

Nutritional Content _____

Food without a choice

If you are a couple, it might also be interesting to surprise each other with one of the foods. This means the partner comes to dinner/lunch completely unsuspecting and has the new food *thrust* on him/her. This is exactly what will happen to your child as he/she arrives at your dinner table. An even more exact experiment for you would be to feed your partner blindfolded, with no time for him/her to analyze what went into the making of this food.

Based on this experience for me, how might my new child respond to these foods?:

• For a 1-year-old: cooked carrot chunks or sticks

_____

• For a 2-year-old: bread sticks or crunchy crackers

_____

• For older children:

plain yoghurt _____

pickles _____

alfalfa sprouts _____

rice cakes _____

fruit leathers _____

What are some things I can predict he/she will like?

_____

_____

_____

_____

_____

_____

_____

Feeding time - a guided imagery

In many orphanages and nurseries there is very little time for adjusting to the child's individual desires about food. This includes whether the child prefers a certain type of nipple, spoon or fork, hand feeding or spoon feeding, little or lots of time between bites or swallows. Did the children eat on the floor, while sitting in a worker's lap, at a table?

Imagine yourself at an orphanage in your child's country. It's feeding time, and there are 20 children in chairs (or cribs) lined up. Stand up in the room you are in and look down the row. You are the principal caretaker and 11 of the children are already crying. They are all toddlers. Somehow you have managed to get them all strapped or seated in place. In front of you are 20 baby bottles, or a big pot of porridge and 20 plastic bowls and spoons. You must feed these children single-handedly. You realize you have half an hour for this meal.

Write your plan here, based on the children's past schedule and experiences.

_____

_____

_____

_____

_____

Questions

1. You may have asked if porridge is <u>all</u> there is. Where are the finger foods? Crackers? Cups of milk? Well, think back to the kitchen in this orphanage, and you can probably imagine why porridge is all... it does contain milk and grains, after all. The question becomes: what are some results in your child's food eating patterns of having had only porridge during the toddler years?

   _____

   _____

   _____

   _____

   _____

2. How will my child react to my/our sitting there all alone with him/her to give such unsolicited and never before experienced attention at meal time?

   _____

   _____

   _____

   _____

3. How might my child react to crispy, crunchy cereals, crackers, vegetable sticks, etc.?

   _____

   _____

   _____

   _____

   _____

Personal experience

If you want a firsthand experience of the changes your child may encounter with you, try it yourself. Yes, eat porridge for a week, breakfast, lunch and dinner (even through a bottle), and add on the elements of eating in silence facing the wall instead of each other, or ask someone to feed you at their (not your) pace. Maybe you'd rather do this experiment for only a day!

Research your child's present feeding habits

For many children, food adjustments from country-to-country are usually no problem. Although many parents notice non-stop eating patterns in their newly arrived children, these usually work themselves out. If, however, your child has some signficant food or feeding problems, to whom will you go for help? Your child's pediatrician may not have all the answers, so use the time now to find local community resources. You will have much less time when your child arrives. Begin by finding the answers to these questions:

1. What are the major repeated foods?

   _____

   _____

   _____

2. What is used for variety?

   _____

   _____

   _____

3. What are considered special treats?

_____

_____

_____

4. How often do we want to use treats and food as rewards or comforts?

_____

_____

_____

5. From reports about my child's present diet/menu of foods, where is he/she getting the necessary vitamins, fiber, protein, etc.? How can I most closely match that in the diet I plan, or how do I plan to make a gradual change?

_____

_____

_____

_____

_____

_____

_____

_____

_____

_____

_____

_____

_____

5
. . . .

Beds and Sleep

Around the world children sleep in a huge range of places. Some children sleep on mats on the floor, some between their parents or foster parents, some in cribs that look like plywood boxes or cages, many in beds of straw mattresses with other children of different ages.

Parents or caregivers in other countries might look askance at North American patterns of isolating children into rooms all by themselves in cribs that look like prison bars where crying can barely be heard and lovemaking by parents kept secret. (This cultural difference statement definitely evokes and deserves some discussion!)

Learn how home environments are different

The question we pose, however, is not necessarily what is right or wrong, but how you plan to make a transition for your child. Indeed it will be a transition. For many adoptive parents who travel to the country of their child's birth and stay in residences or small apartments along with other adoptive couples or with host families, the transition becomes clearer.

A quote from our Vietnam coordinator will illustrate: "Part of your stay at the orphanage guest house will include having the services of a Vietnamese nurse. You may think that you know how to care for a child, and certainly you would in your own house, but it is a *very different* thing here in Vietnam!" Parents who read this statement wonder what he is talking about.

Here is a partial list of child care practices in Vietnam. Read through it, and consider how the practices might apply in your child's country. (If your child is from Vietnam, consider how you might adapt to these practices.)

- Daily airing and cleaning the mats on which babies sleep to prevent infections from parasites
- Washing all bed clothes, diapers and children's clothes during the only two hours a day you have running water
- Using and often changing the thin cloth diapers to prevent heat rash
- Draping all sleep areas with nets to avoid malaria or dengue-fever- bearing mosquitos
- Covering a child from head-to-toe, no matter the temperature, in keeping with local opinion
- Filtering polluted city water, worrying about breathing polluted city air

_____

_____

_____

_____

_____

_____

_____

Questions to ask adoptive parents who have been to the host country

During your adoption education process, most adoption agencies provide you with telephone numbers of parents who have recently traveled to adopt. Some may also have panels of adoptive parents at their training sessions or at conferences for you to attend.

Here are some questions you might ask them.

1. What was the hardest part of taking care of your child while you were in the host country?

_____

_____

_____

2. Did you get sick? Exhausted?

_____

_____

_____

3. How did you feel when you entered the door to your own bedroom upon your return home?

_____

_____

_____

Questions to consider about sleep and beds as you prepare your child's bedroom

1. What is our present plan for helping to ease our child's transition between his/her present sleeping situation and the situation in our home?

_____

_____

_____

2. How long are we expecting this transition to take?

_____

_____

_____

3. What backup plan do we have in mind if the transition does not go well, and we get overtired, have to go back to work too soon, or see patterns in our child that alarm us?

_____

_____

_____

4. What might be patterns that would alarm us?

_____
_____
_____
_____
_____
_____
_____
_____

5. What adjustments might you make as you remove a child from an orphanage where he/she:

- has never slept alone
- has never experienced silence
- may wake up many times each night
- has never been consoled after a night terror

_____
_____
_____
_____
_____
_____
_____
_____
_____
_____
_____

6
· · · · · · · · · · · · · · · ·

Child Development

As with every other "science" of today, child development specialists have prepared lists to measure and test their subjects. According to their lists, a child of 18 months should have mastered a set of about 25 different skills, a child of 24 months will have mastered about 50 gross and fine motor control skills, and so on.

About developmental assessments

Parents who adopt children from other countries often go with these lists in hand or ask questions from them ahead of time. Some countries are now providing developmental assessments of the children for the adoptive families. The results are often extremely helpful in determining and predicting the future for a child, especially children who were born prematurely, who might have cerebral palsy, early childhood seizures, or any possible neurological or cerebral damage.

As helpful as developmental assessments can be, the results can be alarming when adoptive parents find that their child, who has no evidence of previous complications or health problems, does not "perform" every skill on the list.

Developmental milestones in children vary from culture to culture, depending on how parents learn to raise their children.

Examples of differences:

- In countries where a child is always carried on a parent's back, the learning tasks that rely on eye contact will develop more slowly.
- In countries where crawling on floors is unacceptable or unsafe for a child, the age that a child develops arm/leg coordination will be different.
- In countries where all activities take place on one level, children may not have learned spatial concepts, traversing stairs, climbing, using caution in heights, balancing, etc.

Exercise

To "go prepared" to meet your child is to go with open heart and mind, and this is the object of this exercise, which acquaints you with the different developmental goals for children.

Guess the age at which a child might begin these behaviors:
3 months, 6 months, 9 months, 12 months, 18 months, 2 years, 3 years, 4 years, and 5 years.

1. bang toys, use a rattle with vigor   _____
2. laugh out loud   _____
3. pull herself up to stand in her crib   _____
4. creep or crawl   _____
5. walk without help   _____
6. count to 10   _____
7. smile   _____
8. babble or squeal   _____
9. move toys around the room   _____
10. say "mama" or "papa"   _____
11. follow movement by turning head   _____
12. run   _____
13. catch a bounced ball   _____
14. tell you who is a boy/girl   _____
15. let you know what he/she wants   _____
16. walk up and down stairs with help   _____
17. reach for and hold objects   _____

18. like to help   _____
19. finger feed self   _____
20. raise head when lying on tummy   _____
21. name some colors   _____
22. ask questions   _____
23. wave "bye-bye"   _____
24. startle at loud noises   _____

Now, compare your responses with the answers that follow:

24. 3 mos.
18 mos. 19. 12 mos. 20. 3 mos. 21. 4 yrs. 22. 4 yrs. 23. 12 mos.
yrs; 13. 5 yrs. 14. 3 yrs. 15. 18 mos. 16. 2 yrs. 17. 6 mos. 18.
7. 3 mos. 8. 6 mos. 9. 12 mos. 10. 9 mos. 11. 3 mos. 12. 2
1. 9 mos. 2. 6 mos. 3. 9 mos. 4. 9 mos. 5. 18 mos. 6. 5 yrs.

Questions

1. As you were "guessing" to fit the developmental tasks to the usual age of child, on what did you base your answers?

   _____

   _____

2. With a group or partner, go back over some of the tasks and ask yourselves why the child you adopt may not have reached these milestones. Think carefully of what you know about the ratio of caretakers and volunteers; number of children living together; number of toys; amount of one-to-one time with children; safety conditions in the orphanage, nursery or foster home; physical conditions/setup of beds, cribs, play areas, etc.

   Use the U.S. Early Childhood Development Chart on the next page to compare what is average for children who have one-to-one child care from their birth parents. As you complete the exercise, ask yourself the very difficult question: what will happen if my child, who may have missed one-to-one child care, never recovers from some developmental delays? What difference will it make in our lives? In our child's life?

A Check List for Growing Children

At 3 months, does your child:
- turn head towards bright colors and lights
- move eyes in same direction together
- recognize bottle or breast
- respond to loud sounds
- make fists with both hands
- grasp rattles or hair
- wiggle and kick with legs and arms
- lift head and chest while on stomach
- smile
- make cooing sounds

At 6 months, does your child:
- follow moving object with eyes
- turn towards source of sound
- reach for objects and pick them up
- roll from stomach to back
- transfer objects from one hand to other
- play with toes
- help hold bottle during feeding
- recognize familiar faces
- babble

At 12 months, does your child:
- sit without support
- pull to a standing position
- crawl on hands and knees
- drink from cup
- enjoy peek-a-boo and patty-cake
- wave bye-bye
- hold out arms and legs while being dressed
- put objects into container
- stack two blocks

At 18 months, does your child:
- like to pull, push and dump things
- follow simple directions
- pull off shoes, socks and mittens
- like to look at pictures
- feed self
- make marks on paper with crayons
- use 8-10 words that are understood
- walk without help
- step off low object and keep balance

At 2 years, does your child:
- use 2-3 word sentences
- say names of toys
- recognize familiar pictures
- carry an object while walking
- feed self with spoon
- play alone independently
- turn 2 or 3 pages at a time
- like to imitate parents
- identify hair, eyes, ears and nose by pointing
- build a tower of four blocks
- show affection

A Guided Fantasy

Have someone read the following to you as you close your eyes and imagine yourself in this situation:
Have someone read the following to you as you close your eyes and imagine yourself in this situation:

You have been "sent" to live with a tribe of Quechuas on the border of Guatemala/Mexico. There has been little or no preparation for your move, and the only thing you know about the Quechuas is that they live in somewhat jungle/wilderness conditions. You are dropped off, having flown to Guatemala City and been driven for 3 days in an all-terrain vehicle with a driver who does not speak English, but who knows his way. You slept when you could in the back of the vehicle and ate what the driver had brought along or bought from roadside stands along the way.

You are tired, faint from the car exhaust and intense heat, sick to your stomach, have cramps, are afraid to drink the water offered, but you have arrived, and the bumpy rutted roads are behind.

There is a family there to meet you in what looks like a village square. They seem happy to have you. The driver, with the only vehicle in the village, leaves. You look around at the dozen mud-wall, thatch-roofed structures in the village and wonder which one belongs to your family. It is already dusk, you are thirsty, wishing for your long-gone last bottle of Evian. Fear strikes even deeper when you no longer hear any slightly familiar Spanish to ask for "agua" but rather the annoying high-pitched chatter of another dialect. The family is looking you over. They are pretty much in your face cackling at you and you have no idea of how to respond except to try to get some distance and turn your head. As you look to the side, four mules are being led towards you and the four family members.

You watch as the oldest woman in the family, wearing a long woven skirt and sandals, steps on the cupped waiting hand of the father and swings on to the mule to sit upright, bareback, "side saddle" style. The young man then helps the daughter (or perhaps daughter-in-law) of the family onto the other mule. The father then looks at you and motions to the next mule. You have already figured out they have saved the best (and most high spirited) mule for you. No saddle, no bit, just a leather strap for a rein. You are going to ride this mule bareback holding on to a piece of leather and probably clutching the mane. You say to yourself (which doesn't help), "I'll never make it, I can't do this!" But this is expected of you, and how would they know you had never been trained to ride a mule bareback? Maybe it's not a mule. Whatever it is, you see that you have no choice, and you attempt to mount. You sink back to the ground on attempt number one. You look around for a rock, a ledge, something to help you mount. There is nothing. The father, weighing far less than you, finally steps over and hesitatingly but firmly hoists you up and over. There you are, hanging over the mule's back, afraid to right yourself to a sitting position by pulling on its mane. Minutes later, after you have fallen off, been helped back up again, been snickered at, you are seated, trembling, knowing the the mule has your number and is beginning to shift and kick under your weight.

The party starts off, single file. You are second to last, thank heavens. Your mule just seems to follow. Your legs in that position ache, more so because you hold them taut to balance. It is much darker now. The sun here goes down and there is no dusk. It is pitch black; there is no lingering light. You can smell the strong, pungent odor of the oil lamp that some family has lit up front. You think they may not have planned for an evening trip, the oil lamp will go out, the wolves will come out, you will all perish. The mosquitoes are already biting, probably the ones with malaria. You can sense only your mule and the huge rocks he is navigating. The path is like something you might hike in a wilderness challenge course. You wish it were daytime and that you could be hiking rather than balancing on this mule. The youngest man in the family is hiking and holding the oil lamp at the head of the group. Why can't you just get off the animal and walk? (Four hours later you will know why.) You want to lie down on the back of the mule to ease the cramps and pain in your legs. You know you can't. The trail has been ascending for the last half hour, and now, suddenly, you can sense you are in for a deep descent. You've got to hold on or slide over onto your head. How can this mule see not to slip? You start to love him for the little security he gives. You are feeling a little better in spirit, although not in body. It isn't raining, it isn't cold, you are with a family who knows what they are doing. In the distance you hear water, rushing water, very loud. As you approach you hear the young man with the lantern call back in a very high-pitched voice to the father in the rear. Everyone stops. You cannot see anything ahead, but you imagine that the "bridge" or something is out.....

Narrator: "Continue on in your guided fantasy until you cross this river and get to where you are going."

Questions

1. It appears this Quechua family expected that you knew how to ride a mule. Why might they expect that?

   _____

   _____

   _____

2. What other expectations (true or false) might they have had of you?

   _____

   _____

   _____

   _____

3. Think of some other skills you might have been expected to have as you adjusted to living with this family. What might they be?

_____

_____

_____

4. Discuss how fear, the unexpected, feeling estranged, feeling sick, etc. might have hindered your attempts at mastering or attempting the skills expected for living in the jungle.

_____

_____

_____

_____

_____

5. What will be new and strange to the adopted child who comes to live with you?

_____

_____

_____

_____

_____

7
· · · · · · · · · · · · · · · · ·

Preparing for the Abused Child

"No, not our child or any child!" Agencies and social workers and caregivers here and in the child's country all would *like* to say a child has not been abused, but they can never be sure. There is preparation for parents, and here are some suggestions for you to prepare yourselves.

Abuse wears many faces in the world

The first step is to understand the many different cultural meanings of what is labeled as abuse. Abuse, especially abuse of a child, is not a question of a moral issue with clear boundaries. It is a question of *your* child, and how your child may have been affected if someone crossed a personal boundary or limit. The limits are very different for each child and are affected by cultural differences, just as what each child fears (snakes, the dark, riding in cars, Santa, etc.) is personally different for each child.

Any of the following might be labeled "sexual abuse" by us, but may or may not have crossed a boundary for a child at a particular age, or may be acceptable in another culture:

- playing with a child's genitals
- allowing a child to watch adult lovemaking
- leaving adult videos within the reach of children
- using sex language with, to, or in the presence of a child
- allowing children to play sex together

- cleaning a child's penis, anus, vagina, genitals in a way that frightens the child or crosses a boundary of pleasure to abuse.

Talk or write about what you consider to constitute sexual abuse of a child.

_____

_____

_____

_____

_____

_____

_____

_____

_____

Any of the following might be labeled "physical abuse" by us, but not necessarily in the culture of the child...

- slapping a child across the mouth for using bad words
- using a strap on a child's bare bottom to correct disobedience
- shaking a child who is screaming
- putting a match to a child's fingers for stealing
- tying a child to a post
- applying extreme hot packs to a child's muscles.

If you have concerns as you observe your adopted child, you need to ask your country representative to explain the cultural norms and to inquire at the orphanage or foster home.

Did it happen to my child?

1. From what I know about my child's life so far, which of the above might have happened to my child? Check which of the following "risk" factors for abuse you know or suspect:

   ☐ Child was "left" to be someone else's charge.
   ☐ Birth mother has a new "live-in" spouse.

    ☐ Birth parents live under extreme stress.
    ☐ Orphanage or foster caretakers are unsupervised.
    ☐ Older children are in charge of younger children.
    ☐ Caretakers are involved in chemical abuse.
    ☐ Birth family has a history of violence.
    ☐ Birth mother emotionally "abandoned" her child.

2. If abuse did exist in the eyes and emotions of my child, how might we possibly experience the consequences?

_____
_____
_____

How will I respond if my child begins to act out previous abuse?

What will I/we do or how will we react when or if our child does any of the following:

1. Uses language about sexual activities far beyond his developmental stage?

_____
_____
_____

2. Crawls up on my lap and begins to touch my genitals?

_____
_____
_____

3. Is reported from day care as seeking sexual play/abuse with other kids?

_____
_____
_____

4. News of our child's behavior gets to our friends and relatives? *Develop a plan of action: (write one here, just in case).*

_____

_____

_____

_____

_____

_____

5. Treats a sibling or playmate with physical harshness?

_____

_____

_____

6. Tries torturing the family pet?

_____

_____

_____

7. Sets fires when angered?

_____

_____

_____

8. Cowers or seems overly anxious when verbally corrected?

_____

_____

_____

8

• • • • • • • • • • • • • • •

A Special Child

Many adoption programs ask you, as you enter the program, to carefully think through and fill out a medical needs checklist. There are two reasons for this:

1. To remind you that every child comes with a genetic make-up and a tendency towards certain medical problems in life. You do not know what the future holds for your child.

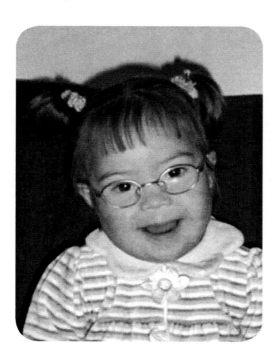

2. To ask you to decide which major identified medical problems you could/would accept in a child referred to you.

If you do not have sufficient medical background (and most of us do not) to understand all of the terminology, use a medical reference book as you fill it out.

Preparing for a child who has special medical needs

Most parents would fill out this checklist very conservatively for handing in to the agency. Many parents would also ask why they should even fill it out. Adoptive parents know that birth parents never get to fill out a list like this. Nevertheless, considering all the possibilities of an ill child is an important part of preparing for adoption.

You might wish to fill it out more than once as you progress through your adoption education and reading. Many parents change their minds about their own capacity to accept a child with special medical needs as they learn more about the children and about adoption. At the end of the list we have added an addendum of additional medical questions. They outline some of the uncommon and unpredictable medical problems adopted children encounter.

Ahead of their child's arrival, most parents ask themselves these questions: What if our child has allergies or constant infections? What if we have an ill child? What degree of illness can our family accommodate? What if our child's illness is chronic or critical? Do not hesitate to share your concerns with your social worker; all of these are good questions to ask *before* your child arrives.

_____
_____
_____
_____
_____
_____
_____
_____
_____
_____

Before the choice of a program or country of adoption, adoptive parents are asked how well they can "handle the unexpected." If their honest answer is "no," then adopting a child over 3-6 months of age may not be recommended for them. International adoption may also not be recommended. How do we stand on accepting the "unexpected"?

_____
_____
_____
_____
_____
_____
_____
_____

List of possible health concerns

Check or highlight the conditions you could accept.

Birth conditions

Prematurity
- 36-40 wks.
- under 36 wks.

Low birth weight
- over 4 lbs.
- under 4 lbs.

Low Apgar scores
Infantile jaundice
Blood transfusion
Slow weight gain

Sucking problems
Poor nourishment
- mild
- severe

Congenital syphilis
Mother known to be Hepatitis B +
Mother known to be HIV or AIDS +
Child known to be Hepatitis B +
Child known to be HIV or AIDS +

Family background concerns

Mental illness in family
background
Chemical dependency
- birth mother
- birth father

Mental retardation
- birth mother
- birth father

Known physical abuse
Known sexual abuse
Born of incest
Born of rape

Developmental conditions

Learning disability (known or
  potential)
- mild
- severe

Hyperactivity
- mild
- severe

Mental retardation
- suspected/minor
- moderate

Speech delay
- mild
- severe

Fetal alcohol syndrome or effects risk
Autism
Down Syndrome

Developmental delay (behind emotionally, physically, and/or socially;
if and when child will catch up is uncertain)
- mild
- severe

Skin conditions

Birthmark
- non-visible when clothed
- on visible part of body
Albinism
Ichthyosis

Missing or deformed ear
Disfigurement requiring correction
Burns needing surgery
- mild
- severe

Medical conditions

Cleft lip
Cleft palate
Cleft lip and palate
Orthodontic problems
Vision
- Strabismus (crossed eyes)
- Nystagmus (roving eyes)
- limited vision
- one eye removed
(normal vision in other)
- blindness
Gastro-intestinal problems
- mild vomiting and/or diarrhea
- severe vomiting and/or diarrhea
- history of mal-absorption
- imperforate anus (with colostomy)
requiring ongoing surgery
- hernia (umbilical and/or inguinal)
Cystic fibrosis
Abnormal genitalia (requires surgery)

Cranio-facial abnormalities
- mild
- major
History of meningitis or encephalitis
Respiratory Problems
- asthma
- active TB
- inactive TB
- other
Hearing
- partial, stable
- partial, unstable
- deafness
Heart Defect
- minor (murmur)
- major defect (affects growth
and activity; needs surgery)
Hydrocephalus with shunt
- reaching developmental milestones
- exhibiting major developmental
delays

Medical conditions, continued

Orthopedic problems
   scoliosis (curvature of spine)
   spina bifida
   walks with crutches, braces
   arthrogryposis
   paralysis/paraplegia
   club foot/feet
   rickets
   partially formed or missing arm
   leg partially formed
   missing or extra fingers
   toes partially formed or missing
   congenital dislocated hip (requires
      casting and/or surgery)
   post-polio
      - mild
      - severe
   stature concerns (markedly small
      for unknown reasons)
      - dwarfism
      - multiple orthopedic problems

Possible incontinence
Kidney malfunction
   - mild
   - severe
Genetic problems or syndromes
Neurological problems
   - seizure disorder
   - single episode
   - controlled with medication
   - currently uncontrolled
Cerebral palsy
   - mild
   - moderate
   - severe
Shortened life-span (terminal
   illness)
Child requiring wheel-chair living
Multiple birth defects

Add any additional medical conditions about which you might be concerned because of your own particuar experiences, such as: allergies to certain foods, pets, pollen, sensitivity to specific chemicals; chronic eye, ear, nose, throat infections; major dental problems; emotional problems such as phobias, behavior disorders, attachment disorder.

_____

_____

_____

_____

_____

_____

_____

_____

How to consider
and share medical concerns

Take a trip to a shopping mall and watch for families with children who have special needs. Observe the family interaction. Put yourself in that family and consider how you would feel in public, how you might feel in the day-to-day care of the child, how your lives might change because of a child who has special needs.

Ask yourselves the hard questions: Would you be angry or resentful? Would it depend on whether or not you knew about the problem before the adoption?

_____
_____
_____

With whom would you feel angry or upset?

_____
_____
_____

Would you consider that the extra care, stress, counting on resources outside your own home would make you a stronger, better family or a family less able to function well?

_____
_____
_____

What is your religious or philosophical belief about having unforeseen things happen or be given to you to deal with?

_____

_____

_____

Give an example of how these principles have already operated in your lives when something unforeseen happened.

_____

_____

_____

_____

Is there anything you would want to change in your own reactions if this happened again?

_____

_____

_____

About kids with special needs who wait *and wait* for adoptive families

Agencies that advocate for children who wait often pose this question to families who wait for a healthy child: Are you limited to a "healthy only" child in the world of adoption
>...because of economic reasons?
>...because of the limits of your medical insurance?

...because of what your relatives might say?

...because you have sustained enough loss in your marriage due to infertility?

...because a perfectly healthy child is part of the dream of most parents?

Which of these is your answer? Or, if none of these is your answer, what might it be?

_____

_____

_____

_____

_____

_____

Develop a philosophy of life about coping with special needs

There is a philosophy that says that parents looking for the perfect baby in adoption are more likely to experience that child in teenage years as very, very difficult and wanting in behavior, temperament, and character. The other side of this adage reveals vignettes of families who opened their arms wide to children with severe medical and emotional needs, and who then lived happily ever after.

From these extremes, put yourselves somewhere on this continuum.

|___|___|___|___|___|___|___|___|___|___|___|___|___|___|

We welcome a child
with special needs   We want
                                          a healthy-only child

Summarize here your philosophy:

We believe...

_____

_____

_____

_____

_____

_____

_____

Now fill in the names of the best medical reference books and specialists in your area that you found in your search. Include those doctors/clinics participating in your medical insurance plan and others in your community.

_____

_____

_____

_____

_____

_____

_____

_____

_____

_____

_____

9

Transitions to Home

Adoptive parents of 3- and 4-year-old children (and up) have described this kind of situation. "We could not believe our eyes. In the morning he awoke before us, dressed himself, pulled the covers back over the bed, folded his night clothes, brushed his teeth, washed his face, and sat quietly awaiting the day." The descriptions range from very early potty training among toddlers to wonderful little housemaids among pre-teen girls. This chapter discusses the well-trained child and also asks you to imagine aspects of your child's present orphanage or foster home residence that contribute to this child's development.

Why children behave "too" well

What is this phenomenon, and how should parents react? We describe a child who is not commonly encountered by adoptive parents, but is nonetheless significant.

This is the "well trained" child who has been "prepared" by a foster family, or who has lived in an institution where there has been a "show house" mentality to impress visitors/potential donors or just to maintain order.

Foster families who prepare older children for adoption, of course, want to do a good job because that will help them keep their jobs. The same is true of many officials of government-sponsored orphanages, who received their positions as political appointments.

In many orphanages, children to be placed for adoption are separated from the children who are there under child protection services and who might be returned to birth parents.

When a sibling group is adopted, the group often comes with a built-in parent. Usually the oldest child has been taught or is self-taught to take care of the rest.

Many amazed adoptive parents later find that children who have been "too well prepared" for adoption need some extra reasons to "just be kids." The oldest sibling "in charge" will often clash with the adoptive mother and be very reluctant or fearful to give up the role of mother/father. The "well-kept" little boy or girl may need some help next to the all-American dirt-catcher friend or birth child in the family.

Discussion

How would you parent a child who is already "a parent"?

_____

_____

_____

_____

_____

What would be your reaction to a child who is too well-trained?

_____

_____

_____

_____

_____

Sometimes adopted children try extra hard to be perfect for their adoptive parents because they subconsciously feel they were not good enough for their birth parents, and they conclude this is why they were "given up." Role play a talk you might have with a child about this.

My child's residence

It is important to learn what you can about the environment in which your child is now living.

Ask if videos of the foster residence or orphanage are available from your agency or from any parents who have recently returned from a visit. Videos often convey much more information than still-photographs or slides; they may show you examples of how the children are treated, how the caregiver relates to them, or give you clues as to the emotional affect of the children.

At the same time, consider how helpful a video of you and your home would be for your future child to see, especially if there is a long wait until she joins your family.

Some questions to help you complete the picture

From the videos or photographs you view or accounts of other adoptive parents, complete the following:

1. Description of the home or orphanage: include toys, bedroom, kitchen, outside play area. (Imagine this if you don't know.)

    _____

    _____

    _____

    _____

    _____

    _____

2. Description of the home/orphanage's caretakers: include numbers of adults and kids, where they physically pass time (offices, play areas, classrooms, outdoors, clinic, etc.)

    _____

    _____

    _____

    _____

    _____

    _____

3. Description of bedtime at my child's present residence: include hygiene, and rituals such as stories, songs, hugs, etc.

_____

_____

_____

_____

_____

_____

4. Description of playtime at my child's present residence: include how many toys are shared by how many children, how frequently they have access to the toys, kinds of toys, are the toys age-appropriate? Are the children given opportunity to have toys of their own?

_____

_____

_____

_____

_____

_____

5. Description of mealtime at my child's present residence: remember what you imagined in Chapter 4, but this time concentrate on clean up or set up.

_____

_____

_____

_____

_____

_____

Discussion

Having completed this imaginary or real visit to my child's present living situation, what adjustments might my child have to make in becoming a member of our household?

For play?

_____

_____

_____

_____

For mealtime?

_____

_____

_____

_____

For bathtime?

_____

_____

_____

_____

For bedtime?

_____

_____

_____

_____

For outings?

_____

_____

_____

_____

In his/her own space?

_____
_____
_____
_____

What climatic adjustments will my child have to make to live with us? What about our pets?

_____
_____
_____
_____

How will a change in the size and layout of living space in our home affect my child?

_____
_____
_____
_____
_____
_____

What adjustments will my child make in transportation? Is my child familiar with the experience of riding in an automobile or a public transportation bus or subway train?

_____
_____
_____
_____
_____
_____

Compare the number of people in my household with the number at the orphanage. How will my child adjust to fewer individuals caring for him/her? What adjustments will I have to make to respond to my child's need for attention?

_____
_____
_____
_____
_____
_____
_____
_____

Are there any noises around our home that may never have been experienced by my child? Check for motors, stereos, fluorescent lamp ballasts, lawn mowers, bug zappers, alarm clocks, etc. How can I introduce my child to the sources of these sounds so that there is no fear of them?

_____
_____
_____
_____
_____

Is our house too silent?

_____
_____
_____
_____
_____
_____

10

· · · · · · · · · · · · · · ·

Enclosed in an Orphanage

As many of us can attest, institutional life might have been good for us at one point in our lives: the college dorm, military training, summer camp experiences. For small children, institutional life is usually not looked upon as beneficial, yet it is the only option in some situations. When living with birth parents results in abuse or neglect, orphanages can become safe havens for children. Your child may have lived in several places, or may have known only institutional life. The most common places for internationally adopted children to have lived are foster homes and orphanages.

Advantages of foster care over institutions

Most child development experts advocate for foster care of a very young child within a small family unit as opposed to care in an orphanage.

These are the reasons:
Foster care in a family setting usually ensures that the child will receive more attention and develop a one-to-one parent/child relationship. In an institution the child must relate to many caretakers on a passing basis. The likelihood of early childhood stimulation (one-on-one play and attention by an adult) is also lower in a large institution. Children often become self stimulating (rocking, head banging) because of this and can miss *learning how to learn.*

A foster family will likely bring the child with them on short trips or on visits to friends. The likelihood of crowded situations in an institution may mean that children stay in their cribs a great deal and stare at the same walls. There is evidence in the research on the developmental process in children that the lack of variety of seeing new sights or seeing objects near and far in varied surroundings affects vision and learning. Foster parents usually enjoy providing their kids with toys and games for play, while in an orphanage there are fewer toys to go around and they are locked up for safekeeping and sharing only at certain times, thus limiting a child's creative play.

A foster home may have a few other children who relate to your children, while in an orphanage setting there is the likelihood that a child is not taught interactive play during playtime, but only experiences how to protect or grab or compete for toys.

Children, as they develop, love to explore their surroundings and to play with adults and other kids. They are eager to explore their limits, e.g. climbing, running, balancing on his/her parent's knee, riding piggy back, playing peek-a-boo. In a crowded orphanage setting with just a few carepersons, exploratory activity is limited, which may result in impaired learning or late learning of spatial-based concepts, problem-solving, etc.

Try to continue this list of differences between foster or family care and orphanage life.

_____

_____

_____

_____

_____

_____

Understanding orphanage care

Parents who adopt an orphanage child should know about the usual care in the orphanage and should go into the adoption knowing of ways to compensate for early developmental delays.

If, for instance, you knew the child you were about to adopt had asthma, you would most certainly have read, consulted, and prepared for this condition. This is what is asked of parents whose children may have missed early childhood stimulation or spatial exploration.

Consider that if your child has not been rocked, cuddled, spoken to softly, heard nursery rhymes, played peek-a-boo or pat-a-cake, or laughed and giggled and cooed with anyone, she/he may take a long time to respond to you, or to sounds, to touch, to movement, to pleasure, or even to pain.

Parents note that children are all different, but that many become extremely excitable in new surroundings with so many toys and sounds and sights--or that they appear stunned. To some children who have no "texture" experience, the cute clothes you put on them, the teddy bears you give them, the food snacks you offer may irritate. To children who have no "vestibular" space-balance experience, having them in different positions to bathe, brush teeth, wash hair, crawl into a playhouse or car seat, use playground equipment, etc. may scare them.

Exercise

Think carefully about the list of differences between institutional living and individual family care for an infant and young child. Try to imagine daily life in this situation for the child. Add your images from other books, articles or videos that you have seen, and try to complete these exercises. They are complete-the-sentence ideas to help you begin to understand the effects of institutional living on a child. (The same may be said of early childhood neglect or abuse from a birth family.)

Questions

1. If I see a child who is hyper-vigilant and cannot relax or trust when I bring him/her toys to play with, a child who seems to always be guarding against impending dangers from without, who does not want to touch or explore things, I might deduce that this comes from:

   _____

   _____

   _____

   Some of the things we might do to counteract this hyper-vigilance are:

   _____

   _____

   _____

   _____

2. If I see a child who appears not to have normal visual perception when given an unfamiliar object or toy, or who appears not to want to examine or play with the toy, or who looks at a toy by squinting, grimacing, looking out of the corner of the eyes, or tilting his/her head, I might deduce that this comes from:

   _____

   _____

   _____

   Some suggestions for helping a child relearn or regain spatial or visual perspective are:

   _____

   _____

   _____

   _____

3. If I see a child who appears to be afraid to be alone at night, or afraid of the dark, I might deduce this comes from:

_____

_____

_____

Some suggestions:

_____

_____

_____

_____

4. If I experience a child who cries over something and cannot be consoled or pushes me away consistently when I try to hold and hug him/her, I might deduce that this comes from:

_____

_____

_____

Some suggestions:

_____

_____

_____

_____

5. If I experience an older child who appears not to have a cause-effect line of thinking (that is, who will put his hand on a hot stove repeatedly, or do something for which he gets punished over and over), I might deduce that:

_____

_____

_____

Some suggestions:

_____

_____

_____

_____

6. If I experience a child who does not distinguish between his/
her body space and the things around him/her (for example,
continues to bump into things, cannot pick up, put down, or
hold things, get out of the way of things, etc.), I might deduce
that:

_____

_____

_____

Some suggestions:

_____

_____

_____

_____

7. If I experience a child who screams or runs away from tickling
or touching, or who appears to be very annoyed at any tactile
play, I might deduce that:

_____

_____

_____

Some suggestions:

_____

_____

_____

_____

8. If a child had spent three to four years in a large group setting where interactive speech was really not used because the children were simply told what to do as a group and never individually talked to, I could expect:

_____

_____

_____

_____

9. If a child had spent one to two years in a large group setting where the majority of time was spent inside cribs with no exploration in a larger play area or outside in a playground, I could expect:

_____

_____

_____

_____

Notes:

It will be helpful in answering the above (quite difficult) questions if you have access to families who have raised children and who can remember at what months of age their children played certain games to help develop the usual skills and traits. Also, thinking of games to play with children (like pat-a-cake, peek-a-boo) will help you understand how children <u>usually</u> learn space, sequence, trust, perception, language, auditory discrimination, etc. If you found the exercises too difficult to answer, you may wish to do some further reading on sensory integration. (See Chapter 21 for additional resources. Books and videos are usually available from local Early Childhood Learning Centers.)

Please understand that these workbook exercises are not intended to scare you, but to prepare you. Adoptive families usually do not encounter all of these difficulties in their children.

11

· · · · · · · · · · · · · ·

Bonding to a Rejected Child

Psychological research indicates that some (but not all) babies who are left unattended in their needs for food, warmth, holding, and attention to their pain or discomfort form a neurological signal system in their brain that in effect says: "No one cares, and I shall have to confront this world all by myself." For that reason, these children do not trust other human beings but rather learn to approach relationships as battles to be won.

These children are sometimes officially diagnosed as having "attachment disorder" or being attachment disoriented. Attachment is described as a feeling between child and parent of being irreplaceable.

Unattached children do not know love and cannot genuinely return love given with hugs and kisses and family closeness. They sometimes give hugs and kisses, but they are not genuine. We do not know the variables of the causes, but we suspect these are babies who are left alone for long periods and frequently during the first year of life. Some are perhaps infants who suffered pain that could not be alleviated or detected, and who therefore felt betrayed and alone in their pain. Some may be children whose pattern of parental care was on-again-off-again as in orphanages or children who are "passed around." There is also increasing evidence that there are genetic and in utero influences on a child's ability to attach, belong, and relate.

With abandoned, abused, and/or neglected children, the possibility of a child suffering from an attachment disorder is obviously higher.

Consequences of early childhood rejection

The continuing refusal to be comforted by physical contact (resisting holding and cuddling) as well as lack of eye or facial contact are serious signs of a lack of bonding and/or attachment. In addition, some older children may exhibit these signs:

- Never developing the normal "stranger anxiety" at the toddler stage that makes them want their mom or dad when left at day care or with babysitters for the first time.
- Wandering off in stores and public places, and never fearing that they are lost or crying for Mom or Dad (up to ages 5-6).
- Treating every stranger or the general public with a sense of being a potential parent, warming up to them in a superficial but manipulative way.
- Never developing a sense of honesty or telling the truth. This can turn into lying in the face of evidence in a very convincing way.
- Not developing a sense of protecting MY family, not protecting siblings, or pets, or property in a way that children usually do if threatened from the outside by other challenges or possible threats.
- Acting threatened by family intimacy or family times or activities together, always wanting to be away, apart, alone in his/her room.
- Appearing to be more comfortable in crowds or with other caretakers than with the immediate family.
- Not feeling remorse for hurting others or learning not to do it again because "it hurts."
- Not being able to understand how what he/she does can affect his/her future. (This is because there was no consistency in associating things like hunger=feeding, wet diaper=changing, cold=cover, fear=comfort, etc.)

Fortunately, there is help available from an increasing number of trained therapists who can assist families when their children are still young enough to reprogram mistrust into a family bond of love and caring. There is no "quick fix," but there is progress.

Attachment problems are not all permanent, not all the same, not all severe. Using the model of a fulcrum, good attachment resides in the center. To one side are children pulling away from closeness/intimacy. On the opposite side are children anxiously clinging to parents and fearing any distancing or independence. Children can also exhibit uncertain or ambivalent attachment and vacillate between the two extremes.

The best "window of time" for treating a child with attachment disorder is before age 4, but therapists are developing good family programs for older children.

Families who travel to receive their adopted child might easily panic if their child reacts to them in a negative way at the first meeting and even for several days or weeks after the placement. Many families recount their fears, disappointments and anguish when there is not "love at first sight." However, some early rejection is normal and even healthy for a child and may not be a sign of lack of bonding. Therapy includes recuperating what a child has missed in infancy--holding, cuddling, and loving eye contact, as well as allowing a child to rage while continued comfort is shown.

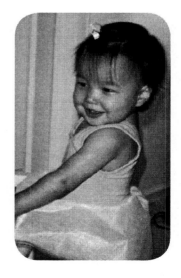

For the greatest number of families, these fears are alleviated quickly as their child "warms up" to them and they learn how to please, delight, and trust each other.

Some practical suggestions
for preparing to meet your child

Here are some practical suggestions of how to prepare for the first meeting:

1. Consider the age your child will be when you first meet. Then find some friends or new acquaintances who have children that very age or a bit younger.

   Observe any of the following as you react to the child. Ask about, and write your definitions or explanations of them:

   stranger anxiety

   _____

   _____

   the terrible twos

   _____

   _____

   self/other awareness

   _____

   _____

   mine/yours approach to toys

   _____

   _____

   the power of "no"

   _____

   _____

   control issues

   _____

   _____

2. Consider what toy you might bring to help you and the child share and warm up to each other. If you can, check out your choice with the child's caregivers ahead of time or ask for suggestions. (We remember calling a family who was on their way to the airport with an extremely important message we had just received from the person escorting the child home: "She is afraid of stuffed animals." The family quickly rearranged their child's bedroom and hid the teddy bear they were going to present at the first meeting.)

3. Pictures of you sent ahead of time (in flexible soft frames or albums, or attached to toys) will help both the caregivers and your child to begin to know you. Again, check out how children your child's age and sex look at photos and what attracts them about a picture, e.g. closeups or detail, small or large, the kind of frame or book. For older children, videos of future sights, pets, siblings, room, school, as well as parents will probably be helpful and are worth some careful thought. When we listen to panels of now older adopted kids relate their first experiences of meeting their families, they almost always note some small detail of the reunion—the shoes they brought me, the stuffed animal they gave me ahead of time that matched the one they brought with them.

4. When children are pre-verbal they rely heavily on their senses of touch and smell. Although it may sound a little extreme, some families have slept with a stuffed toy a few nights before they wrap it up in plastic to send to their soon-to-be-adopted baby to get used to the smell of his or her new mom or dad.

5. Continue to brainstorm and store your ideas here: what might we do to help the bonding between us and our child?

_____

_____

_____

_____

_____

_____

_____

_____

_____

Ways to encourage attachment when your child comes home

You will instinctively find ways to encourage attachment once your child is with you at home. It is also wise to think and prepare ahead of time. The following suggestions come under the three categories of reacting to your child's patterns, initiating/teaching new behaviors and techniques that might help your child adjust and attach.

Responding to your child if your child goes to just "anyone":

*   Find ways to reward her in public for being close to you, e.g. bring along treats, whisper special things to her, etc.

*   Spend more time at home and only gradually bring him to parties and public places where others will exclaim over him.

*   Go to places with your child where she would naturally seek your protection or needs to be held, e.g. swimming, boating, rides, and skating.

If your child appears to distance herself from your family:

- Practice or make a ritual out of using "mom," "dad," "my brother," etc.
- Use statements like: "In our family, we...," " your grandmother says...."
- Use relatives, especially grandparents, as models of closeness, hugs, gifts, family jokes, and sayings.
- Share family treasures, places of importance, secret playing places. Make the family room less of a TV room and more of a game or "together" room.
- Be the visible "mom" or "dad" that helps in school or leads a group important to your child.
- Do things together as a family that most families would do separately: shop for clothes, gifts, grocery shop, greet the school bus together, do sleepouts in the family room, bake together, finding moments in all of this to embrace or hold your child.

If your child seems to want too much independence:

- Make a bigger thing than usual out of a small cut or bruise or minor illness as an opportunity to be close.
- Make a bigger thing out of comforting at a crying or sad moment.
- Defend a child more against an "outside bully."
- Make an important excuse for tucking your child into bed, helping him/her dress, bathe, etc.
- Stay with your child at the doctor's or dentist's office.

If your child tries to distance himself by not wanting to talk about his past, his culture or his new family:

- Try frequent personalized comments about his worth; for example, "You are such a good artist, your birth parents must have talent," "You must have had good art lessons in the orphanage," etc.

- Find out about his achievements from others and make a big deal out of them.

- Share stories about your child's culture as if you knew some personal things about him before he arrived.

Enlarge this list:

_____

_____

_____

_____

_____

_____

_____

_____

_____

_____

_____

_____

_____

_____

_____

_____

12
. . . .

Separating from Caretakers

No amount of preparation, of gifts, of previous attempts at connecting can prepare some children for the separation and loss that an adoption and the move to a new country and family causes them. Children may be very good actors and can be easily distracted for short periods of time by the fairytale-like atmosphere of hotel life during the adoption process, but many fear and mourn leaving what they have known all their lives. Comparing an adoption parting to going off to college or going off to

camp are simply not valid comparisons. Internationally adopted older children have no conceptual framework for time, space, or place comparisons. Adoption and having a new family is for most children a total unknown as is their new home, and so is the reaction of the child. It may be smooth, it may be covered and guarded, or it may be tumultuous. You as parents need to try to be prepared.

Anticipating the changes your child will experience

Here is a list. Rank the items in the order you think would make the <u>most</u> difference in a change for your child at his/her age and circumstances. Compare your ranking with your partner.

___ Change of language
___ Change of food
___ Change of landmarks
___ Change of caretakers
___ Change of daily routine
___ Change of playmates (from many to ? at home)
___ Change of smells
___ Change of familiar clothes (bed clothes, bath towels, etc.)
___ Change of expectations from caretakers
___ Change of possessions (what is "mine")

A Guided Fantasy

Ask someone to read the following account of a move aloud to you. During the reading, close your eyes and do your best to imagine yourself about to join a new family.

As you hear this you are either at home, or tonight you have a home to go to. You can picture your bedroom now. You know where your things are, you know where in that home you feel most comforted, cozy, supported. You know how to drive there, use your key to get in, turn on the lights, get a snack from the kitchen, and get ready for a night's sleep.

However, tomorrow night you will not be going back there. Instead, you will be brought to a new house, to a new family, to sleep in a different bed, with different people... forever. You will be transported by plane and then by car, and it will be impossible for you to memorize the route or even know where you are. You'll be very, very tired from the trip. You'll have a headache or dizziness or a feeling that your body is not adjusting well to so many changes.

You'll be given a tour of your new house. The house smells strange. You are so tired you won't remember the rooms or how to get back to them. You won't know which ones are yours and which ones are theirs. You'll be shown your bedroom, and you'll be left alone in it. You'll be hugged and kissed lots, and it will feel very, very strange

The way to the bathroom will be different, the way to turn on lights and water all changed. You'll wonder why these new people won't just leave you alone, or why they have left you alone.

The TV or radio you hear will no longer be in the language you know. It will be a cacaphony of sounds that makes no sense to you whatsovever, and you will therefore not know things like the time of day, the day of the week, the weather report, or the sometimes comforting evening local news that keeps you in touch with your reality.

There will no longer be phone calls to or from your friends or relatives. You will be too far away and won't know how to connect or use the phone system.

The kitchen will have food, but nothing you recognize or know how to prepare. You won't know what's theirs and what's yours. You'll begin to want to take food you see and recognize to your room, something to have "just in case."

Your bed and bedroom will be well-furnished, with all new clothes and toiletries, but the smells will all be "new" and you'll miss where you came from in a strange and unexplainable way. You wonder how you'll look and feel in these strange new clothes.

You curl up in this new bed and cover your head and close off the sounds and the smells and the fear of the strange newness. You wish you could just sleep it off.

Share with your partner/group how this story made you feel. Make adaptations for your child and try to imagine his/her story. Talk about anything that you can do to help.

Notes:

_____
_____
_____
_____
_____
_____
_____
_____

_____
_____
_____
_____
_____
_____
_____
_____
_____
_____
_____
_____

The stages in a child's grief/loss/separation

An adopted child moving from foster care, an orphanage, or nursery to your home is undergoing a major change. The word "change" can be synonymous with loss, even though neither the child nor you as parents would want to think of this change as a loss. But it is a loss of the past, no matter if the past was good or not, and if your child shows signs of grieving this loss, you will want to be able to recognize and understand them. The signs described here are adapted from the classic loss and grief stages described by Elizabeth Kubler-Ross who first recorded them from the experience of the death of a loved one.

1. Denial

Your child begins to miss what he has left behind, but throws himself into the distractions of the new life to deny his feelings. Obviously, this is not hard to do, as there are so many new things to experience, people to meet, fun to have, toys to experience. The new life is a veritable fairyland, and yet, after a while, you may notice any of these signs:

- clinging to a particular object and refusing to share, give it up, put it away, and throwing temper tantrums over it

- if your child is escorted to you, extreme acting out at the airport, refusing to leave the escort, crying, screaming, etc.

- having flat emotions, not showing either joy or sadness, appearing depressed or aloof, and trying to control her reactions, being over-compliant

- using rhythmic behavior such as rocking, tapping, banging, or masturbation as emotional release; asking or wanting things over and over again

- refusing to eat, sleep, participate in required or invited activities.

- developing real or imagined illnesses, being susceptible to accidents, injuries

- refusal to talk about the past, look at photos, etc.

Some important responses by parents

Here is a starter list. Continue it with your own ideas:

- Reassure your child
- Help name the feeling

- Provide other rhythmic opportunities (e.g. ball games, musical instruments, rocking chair, swing)
- Provide surroundings for child to feel safe (and private) while eating, sleeping
- Let your child use a toy, pajamas, or other items from her past

_____

_____

_____

_____

_____

_____

_____

_____

2. Trying to fix it

In this stage your child is having an inner dialogue or bargaining session with herself, saying, "If I do this, probably my feelings of loss will just go away." It is a stage of trying to fix what really is not fixable. Some possible outward behaviors you might observe:

- Imaginary conversations, talking to self, not appearing to connect verbally with anyone outside
- frustration with not understanding or speaking this new language trying to make things "perfect" on the outside
- doing things on purpose to get "kicked out" of this new family (with the hopes of reverting to the old)
- if talking with an outside person who understands and speaks his language, may make up outlandish stories about the present family or past abuses, orphanage practices, etc. as a way to control the scenarios

Some important responses by parents

Here is a starter list. Continue it with your own ideas.

- Consistently remind children that no matter what they do, they are accepted and will not be kicked out.
- Put emphasis on their feelings about the stories they "make up" rather than on the content of the stories.
- Give permission and model showing that things and behavior do not have to be perfect.
- Concentrate on the sucess of new words in the new language.
- Spend quiet times together, with lots of non-verbal communication.

_____

_____

3.   Anger at this feeling of loss not "going away" or "being fixed"

In this stage you will notice some definite acting out and angry feelings, either by outbursts or the opposite, depression. If we kept our own diary of anger, we would have to admit that our anger mostly comes from someone not doing what we wanted them to do, or anger with ourselves for not performing the way we wanted to. The loss of self esteem in not being able to make things go the way we want them to can result in _anger in = depression_, or _anger out = acting out_. Here are some signs of what you will see:

- hurting or destroying people, pets, objects
- losing, misplacing, being careless of possessions
- self-destructive, mutilating self
- bed wetting, soiling
- defiance and disobedience

- learning and using swear words, talking back
- regressing to infantile or animal-like behavior
- temper tantrums, whining, crying
- sexually aggressive or provocative behaviors

For depressed children:
- whine and cry continuously
- give up easily or refuse to try anything
- distracted, cannot pay attention, do not want to participate
- difficulty accomplishing earlier mastered tasks

Possible responses by parents

Here is a starter list. Add your own ideas to it.

- Give the child permission to feel anger as normal.
- Help the child express anger on a pillow, punching bag, etc.
- Teach anger control by consistent patterns of consequences, e.g. having the child sit next to you. (Note: for a child who fears being abandoned, time-outs in her room may NOT be effective.)
- Calm the child with a peaceful tone of voice and lack of shock reaction.

_____

_____

_____

_____

_____

_____

_____

_____

4. Understanding and coping

As parents, you will know and appreciate when your child begins to understand that he has not been "himself" and wants to move on to being and feeling normal again.

It is important to know that these stages pass, happen again and again in a child's life, and cannot be controlled by you, the parents. Many adoptive parents take great precautions to make sure their child does not "relapse" by safeguarding them from seeing visitors from their old orphanage, former foster parents, even classmates at gatherings. Other parents consider it important to help the process of moving on by phone calls back to the country, letters, pictures, reunions, etc.

As parents, trust that you will know what is best for your child when the time comes.

5. Resignation/Acceptance

At this stage your child will not only have understood the feelings of sadness and loss, but will have accepted the fact that these feelings come and go during life. We, as adults who have experienced the death of a parent or loved one, can liken this stage to our own feelings of sadness and loss that repeat and come in waves. Certain days or objects or persons remind us of this sadness, (for an adopted child this is often Mother's or Father's Day, a birthday, an experience that reminds him/her of the long past, etc).

Do not, however, expect a child to reach this stage until young adulthood or even later. Until then, your adopted child may often feel and act out feelings of loss and grief without knowing what has set them off or how to deal with them.

13

• • • • • • • • • • • • • • • •

Travel and Culture Shock

Most countries require that the parents travel to the country and personally meet their child and then formally petition the adoption to the court, to a government official, or to a government committee. In some countries, one or both parents are required to wait for the court filing to be granted and a final adoption decree to be issued and then obtain a new birth certificate, passport and visa to travel. Because adoptive parents range from those who have never traveled outside the U.S. to those who have lived for months and years in other countries, there are varying reactions and acceptance of this policy.

The importance of travel and time in the country

Most agencies believe this requirement is best for the child for the following reasons:

• Meeting your child where he/she is and has been living gives you invaluable insight into how to make the transition to your family.

• Meeting your child before the adoption allows you to see for yourself your child's health and development.

• In some countries, meeting the birth mother or the foster family is possible and may create that vital link for your child when he/she is older and wants to know more about his/her roots, even if only by pictures and videos you took at the time.

• Staying in the country allows you as a family to absorb the culture, the sounds, something of the language, and to hopefully fall in love with your child's people, customs and culture.

• Your attempt and trials at enculturation, language, and adapting to a lot of change at once can give you some insights into what is happening to your child during the move.

The differences between vacation and travel to adopt your child

Travel and stay in a country for adoption are very different than travel for a vacation or for pleasure. These are the elements that make them different.

During a vacation you are:
*   usually in control, and can leave if you don't like it.
*   carrying and needing to care only for your luggage as your "belongings."
*   there to relax and see the sights.

During an adoption stay you are:
*   feeling vulnerable because the courts and the "system" are in control of your time and make decisions that affect you.
*   caring for a child, with others watching you do things for the first time, in a country where child-rearing practices are most likely very different than yours.
*   eager to return home, no matter how much you may try to distract yourself by sightseeing and shopping.

Tips

Most parents find the following comforting and valuable when traveling to adopt:
*   Engage in social time with the in-country representative or host. Friendships (based on trust and the need for the services of the host) can last a long time past the adoption. However, when there are several adoptive families, parents can become protective of the representative's time and friendship. They begin to express complaints about inefficiency and lack of services. A relaxed, accepting frame of mind is the best preventative. Remember that customs and values differ greatly from culture to culture and a country representative's viewpoint of the process is probably much different from yours.

Talking to other adoptive parents ahead of time who have been through the country stay and spent time with the representatives and/or host families is advisable.

- Treasure your time alone with your new child and spouse (if married). Parents refer to this as the honeymoon stage of the adoption after the first excitement and acceptance of their child has occurred. It is a quiet and wonderful bonding time for a family, free of visitors, at-home family obligations, and the daily time-consuming tasks of providing for a family. This period, if it stretches beyond the normal limit of a few weeks, can, however, turn into a trial-by-fire between spouses who feel they are stranded in the country. They begin the sometimes fruitless task of "seeing what they can do" to move the system.

- Form friendships with other adoptive parents (while resisting the tendency to compare or compete with them). Friendships formed during adoptions are one of the reasons for the existence of nationwide groups often called "Parents of Children from _____." As their children grow up, these parents will travel thousands of miles to have a summer get-together. The experiences they had together with their new children in the adoption country can be remembered and revisited with none other than these same families.

Notes:

We (I) consider the above important, and our goal during our adoption in-country is:

_____

_____

_____

_____

To prepare for your trip to a country, travel notes, and travel tips are often available from your adoption agency, Internet web sites, or parent support groups. These are always a good idea to read but also to question: Will my stay be the same?

Tips such as, "Don't take a fold-up stroller because there are virtually no sidewalks to walk on," or "Bring a snuggly or front pack for your child because that is what he/she is most used to with the foster family," may be helpful, but be sure they apply to your situation. Because we know you will be able to get these ever-changing lists, we do not include them here, but rather encourage you to turn to a different kind of preparation. This is the kind of preparation that parents often forget: the preparation for culture shock.

Am I a candidate for culture shock?

Rate yourself on each of the following statments using a scale of 1-10.

____ My sense of humor is good in stressful situations.
____ I am curious about other ways of life.
____ I am open-minded (versus opinionated).
____ I am laid-back, not task-oriented.
____ I am self-reliant, independent.
____ I have a high tolerance for noise and commotion.
____ I have a strong sense of myself (I can be made fun of and enjoy it).
____ I can show affection with my extended family and friends.
____ I can reach out to those in plights or poverty.
____ I can ask for help.
____ I am flexible about time.
____ I am tolerant in ambiguous situations.
____ I have the ability to fail and have experience in this area.
____ I can figure out why things might be like they are.
____ I like to go camping.

My score _____ (A score of 100 is considered good.)

How much do I know about my child's culture-of-origin?

You know the answers to these questions in your own culture. You may know some answers about your child's country. Save the unanswered questions for discovery while you spend time in the country and have the opportunity for extended conversations and observations.

- Who gets married or lives together, and why?
- How many live under one roof? What is the pecking order?
- Where, how, and how often do extended family and friends interact?
- Who takes charge of the "run-away sheep" in the family?
- How are children age 2 disciplined?
- How are children age 8 helped to become interested in school?
- How are teenagers controlled?
- Who does sex education and how much is provided?
- What do people learn from TV?
- What does a religious holiday (choose one) look like when celebrated?
- What does a national holiday (choose one) look like when celebrated?
- What is a typical superstition?
- What does "Joe Average" think of the police?
- What do the poor think of the government?
- How do the poor treat the rich on the subway/buses?
- How do the rich treat the poor on the streets?
- Who would get vocational training?
- How do people react to public breastfeeding?
- Is there legal prostitution?
- What drugs are illegal?
- How do people view lawyers, doctors, teachers?
- What do people believe about the press?
- What is the up-and-coming profession?
- Who gets special education? Occupational therapy?

- Who goes to psychiatric clinics and for what?
- What are three favorite pastimes?
- What is the one thing money can't buy?
- Where do people go for spiritual answers?

Glancing at ourselves in a mirror

This is an exercise in preparation for travel. Some people of other cultures may view you through very different eyes, and it may well make a difference in your feelings when you meet them. The following have been said about North Americans. How potentially damaging (and true) do you consider them? How prevalent do you think they are in the country you will visit for your adoption? Consider how these views might affect you during your stay in the country.

- Americans have an insatiable drive to subdue, dominate, and control the environment.
- They equate change with improvement.
- They are so action-oriented they are "hyperactive" and cannot even take a vacation without mixing some work with it.
- Being action-oriented has made them superior at problem-solving; what is worse, they think every problem has to be solved rather than lived.
- Because they are so "in control" of their friendships, family ties are relatively weak in the U.S. People actually appear distant and cool.
- Americans are so anti-authoritarian that even when they are in supervisory roles they insist on being called by first names.
- Money seems to be the only kind of motivation they have.
- They are hurried and harried.
- They are all wealthy compared to us.
- While they are disrespectful of authority, most blindly obey the law.
- They are wasteful.
- They are loud and rude.

- Americans are hard-working.
- They are generous.
- They have all the answers.
- Their society is laced with racial prejudice.
- They are ignorant of other countries.
- They are not conscious of class-distinction.
- They don't respect age or experience.
- North Americans tend to be violent. They are too fond of guns.

Questions

Which of all these views about North Americans would most affect me?

_____

_____

_____

_____

_____

_____

What might I do to "be careful" or to offset a negative view or prejudice?

_____

_____

_____

_____

_____

_____

_____

_____

_____

What feelings do we think our child (or caretaker) may already have about North Americans? From what you've learned about his/her country-of-origin, are they understandable?

_____

_____

_____

_____

Can you identify some of your own prejudices? List them here.

_____

_____

_____

_____

_____

_____

_____

14

Home and Post-adoption

Last year a parent staying in Colombia for her second adoption reflected on going home with another new child and what it would be like. I was surprised at her answers, but I have come to believe that they represent what a lot of adoptive parents go through when the euphoria of the airport "welcome home" by family and close friends has finished.

This chapter helps prepare you for coming home and provides some suggestions for rituals for your new family to celebrate and state your new "passage."

Some observed truths

Here are one parent's post-adoption reflections:

First: Very few people understand what you have been through. You should seek out other adoptive parents to talk to, rather than those who have never been through an adoption. Others don't understand the fears, the waiting, the lack of control, the culture shock of new and unfamiliar sights, smells, expectations, etc.

Second: Lots of people still don't know how to "normalize" the presence of an adopted child. They meet your child and they talk about "differences" because they can't use the usual new-baby phrases such as, "He looks just like you!" At work your boss sends flowers to the hospital to mothers who give birth. You don't get any. It would mean a lot to you if others didn't consider your family *so different.*

Third: There are no "personal questions" asked the way they are asked about a birth. Even men know how to ask more questions about pregnancy and delivery than about adoption. Unless your friends and relatives have some knowledge of your child's country and culture, they will have few meaningful questions to ask.

Fourth: No one would ever expect post-partum depression from an adoptive parent, but post-placement depression does exist and does happen to new adoptive parents.   It can be a combination of

- reverse culture shock, not quite being able to re-adjust to coming back,
- the let-down after it's all over,
- physical fatigue, lingering illness,
- adjusting to new and sometimes overwhelming responsibilities of parenthood.

Because most adoptive parents never show this private "down" side to their lives, because the euphoria of being new parents often buoys them up for a long time, the honeymoon of adoptive parenthood often appears to last and last.   For some it does.   However, the prepared parent will at least have asked the questions and thought about the reality of post-adoption adjustment.

Exercise

From knowing yourself and your reactions to returning from vacation travel, going back to work/school, etc., answer the following questions.

1. What will it be like to walk back into our house after a long absence? What will take up my time and concerns?

   _____

   _____

   _____

   _____

2. How might I adjust to a new social schedule of friends and family wanting to meet our new child?

   _____

   _____

   _____

   _____

3 How will I react when our new child misbehaves in front of company?

_____

_____

_____

_____

4. How will I react when our new child gets ill?

_____

_____

_____

_____

5. What aspect of parenting do I feel the most unprepared for?

_____

_____

_____

_____

6. What resources will I use for help? Examples can be friends, relatives and neighbors.

_____

_____

_____

_____

Your child's adjustment

Just as you may experience post-adoption let-down, your child is experiencing a whole series of adjustments:
- Everything is new.
- Nothing is the same.
- Everyone has expectations about me.
- Everyone is looking at me.

- I am afraid to try all these new things. (I don't want to fail *again*.)
- I lost my past, the only thing familiar to me.

Your child may feel sad, resentful, and guilty at the same time.

Family rituals to help a new child

All changes in life need celebration or mourning, a public statement, and a vehicle for people to express what they are feeling. We know this from our religious rites. We also know that the U.S. has fewer rituals than most countries and that it is up to us to create what we need. Because rituals serve to define "belonging," non-traditional families need them even more than others.

Here is a list of some possible family projects and rituals that might help all of you "claim" each other as family members. The list is a starter; brainstorm to come up with more projects. (Complete rituals usually have the elements of special place, words or music, symbols, gifts, clothes, being public or inviting guests, having a leader, facilitator or master-of-ceremonies, or singling out the guest of honor.)

1. Have a family picture taken soon after you get home and get it developed. Have all members there as you put it up on the wall. Begin to hand out copies.

2. Send out adoption announcements. Let your child play a role in the project.

3. Present your child to your faith community in a ceremonial way.

4. Help your child learn important names and addresses... your home address, your phone, the names of grandparents, cousins. If your child is old enough, help him/her start an address/phone or photo book of these people and places.

5. You may want to create a welcoming ceremony at your home for your child, perhaps lighting a candle together or sharing a special meal. You can take photos of the ceremony and send them back to the child's country, or make a videotape to send back to his caretakers. It is usually not advisable to subject a new child to exposure at large gatherings of people.

Add your own project ideas.

6. _____

_____

_____

7. _____

_____

_____

A parent pledge

At the same time that your child begins this lifelong adjustment to you as a family, parents are asked to renew their commitment to their child. Read and sign the following:

1. As a parent of an adopted child, I know that I must be physically and psychologically available to this child, more so than as a parent of a birth child. I will take this time and energy.

2. As the parent of a child who comes with a *past,* I know that I must listen to this past and refrain from too much advice-giving that comes out of my culture, my country, and my own past.

3. As a parent of a child who has many feelings of loss and confusion about what has happened, I know that I must help him/her find words for these feelings and express them, no matter how much those feelings may affect me.

4. As the parent of a child who has already had one or more caretakers and lived in one or more "homes," I recognize that I will not be able to be all things and the *only one* for my child. I will need support persons in my life and so will my child. I will look for and identify these key people.

5. As the parent of a child who will need to cope with loss and to grieve for what will never come true for him/her, I know that I will need to both normalize these feelings and acted out behaviors, and that I will need to set limits for my child. I promise to neither ignore nor destructively control my child's adoption issues.

6. I know that later on in life my child might experience any of the following due to his/her adoption:

   • Feel disconnected/unattached to a family
   • Think "I must be bad because I do bad things"
   • Feel rejected for no obvious reasons
   • Feel a lack of control over his/her actions
   • Wonder who he/she really is, and have no answer
   • Have difficulty in friendships/relationships/intimacy
   • Be generally mad and angry at the world

As a parent, I know that adoption is a far better solution for children needing permanency than institutional life, foster care, or care by biological parents who do not want them. Yet, I also know that adopted children often need more specialized care than biological children. I am prepared for this and will do my best to provide for my child.

Signature _____

Signature _____

15

. . . .

Preparing for Prejudice and Being Different

Adoptive families are different because they comprise a minority. If they comprise a minority, then there is a definite possibility of prejudice, if not because of racial differences among their children, then because of adoption itself. This chapter helps parents become aware and prepare for what may become a minor or perhaps major element of the adoptive child's life.

The experience of being pre-judged

Prejudice? The dictionary defines prejudice as an irrational attitude of hostility directed against an individual or group or their supposed characteristics. Prejudice is usually not based on facts or reality. It is often used to justify other emotions, such as fear, frustration, and projection of anger at something else.

The topic of prejudice is probably the most frequently published and publicized aspect of adoption. For that reason, we will not dwell on it at length, but you may extend your discussions if you wish. Here are some exercises to use.

A situation:

Between your child's second and third grade years in school you move to a different part of the country because of a job change. Your child comes home from the second week of school crying about something among his new friends/foes/classmates, and he will not tell you what it is. Write here the questions you might ask or the guesses you might suggest to help him open up to what happened. Put his/her possible responses down also. (Or, if you are in a group or doing this with your partner or support person, role-play the scene).

You:

_____

_____

Your child:

_____

_____

You:

_____

_____

Your child:

_____

_____

You:

_____

_____

Your child:

_____

_____

Dealing with teachers

Next, devise and write down your plan of how you might deal with the teacher, principal, school counselor or other children. Don't just talk about it, but close your eyes and put yourself in the scene and let fly whatever words come out. Write them down. Replay the scene with a different audience or at a different time; do this several times. When you have some responses on paper, talk about them and analyze them.

What I said to or asked the teacher:

_____

_____

_____

_____

What I said to my child:

_____

_____

_____

_____

What I asked my child's older sister/brother about the scene:

_____

_____

_____

_____

What I said to or asked the school counselor:

_____

_____

_____

_____

How I described it to my own mother (and the advice she gave me):

_____

_____

_____

_____

Some hard questions about prejudice in general

You are on a panel of adoptive parents at a national or local adoption conference. Any one of these questions is directed to you. What would you answer?

1. Some Caucasian parents pay highly inflated adoption fees or wait years and years to get a child hand picked from "X" country because the children are Caucasian. What is your opinion about this and how those children may fare in their adoptive families?

   _____

   _____

   _____

   _____

   _____

2. We are not prejudiced against children of a different color but the community in which we live is. Members of our extended family think our child should share some family resemblance. Is there any problem in requesting a child that looks like he/ she is our birth child?

   _____

   _____

   _____

   _____

   _____

3. What happens to you as parents when you see your child (of a different color) as an object of prejudice? What did you do to prepare your child beforehand for what he/she might encounter?

_____

_____

_____

_____

_____

4. Have you thought or would you ever think of moving to a different ethnic neighborhood for your adopted child's sake? Why, or why not?

_____

_____

_____

_____

_____

5. (To parents of adopted teens) Who are your child's friends? Who does your child date? How did these friendships happen? Do you approve of them?

_____

_____

_____

_____

_____

Feeling different

The following are 10 possible "inner" statements (ones parents may never hear) that an adopted child between ages 10-12 might harbor.

Rank them from 1 (this doesn't seem to apply) to 10 (this describes my child's attitude exactly) in the order you think describes your child's own feelings. Put yourself in your child's place and try to imagine as best you can.

____   1.   I don't look like anybody in this family.

____   2.   They don't know what it's like to be alone in this family.

____   3.   I don't feel pretty/handsome at all. I feel ugly.

____   4.   I feel as if I do not fit in my adoptive family.

____   5.   It's difficult for me to make friends at school because I'm not like the other kids.

____   6.   My parents treat me differently than they would treat their "own" kids. The standards set for me to attain are different.

____   7.   Other people can "tell" I'm adopted. I can never hide it.

____   8.   Some day I want to return to my "own" people/country.

____   9.   I feel somehow special because I was adopted.

____   10.   Why is it that adopted kids always have to be loners?

____   11.   I feel as if I always have to prove myself to other people.

____   12.   I wish I was still with my "real" mother. I wonder if I'd feel happier?

____   13.   Sometimes I feel like running away.

____   14.   I'm not part of this family; I'm only living here.

____   15.   Only other adopted kids can become my "real" friends because they alone know what it's like.

Adoption is not the cause of every problem

Parents, relatives, teachers, therapists, and society in general can often see, blame, or look to adoption as the cause of all problems in a child's life.

As parents, you may become sensitive to this prejudice and your sensitivity can help others as well as your child.

With your group/spouse, discuss any of the following:

- Why the media overplays adoption in the case of a family murder, violence or abuse

- How programs such as "adopt a highway" might make children who were adopted feel

- How to deal with strangers who approach you and single out or ask about your "adopted child"

- The myth that "adoptive parents adopt to save poor little children, and therefore these children are lucky and should be forever grateful"

- The myth that "people adopt children for farm hands, house servants, or for organ transplants"

- The myth that because adoptive parents more easily view their adopted children as "objects," physical and sexual abuse occur more frequently in these families

16

· · · · · · · · · · · · · · ·

Siblings in Adoption

When siblings are adopted together, or when a new adoptive child joins children who become his/her siblings, the dynamic is different from that of the first child in a family.

This chapter is intended to help families look at the relationships among siblings. It also considers the sometimes difficult question of whether a new adopted child should always be the youngest, or whether two unrelated children should be adopted at the same time.

The significance of birth order in the family

If we look at the order of children in a family, we note a few important principles in the development of the egos of children.

1. The first-born child in a family has the special place of eldest in the family, a place that he/she is usually reluctant to relinquish.

2. In some families, eldest means the first expected to leave the nest, the example to the rest, the one on whom the parents learned how to parent, the protector, the one who makes the family name in school and business.

3. If being "first" is changed by the arrival of an older adopted sibling, extra preparation of the child who will be "re-placed" in the family order needs to be done. Many times adoption social workers will recommend against changing the family order. However, the decision is more commonly based on what the adoptive parents say about the age, security, and character of the presently oldest child. In instances where the now older child already

looks to older cousins or neighbors for direction and security, there may be less adjustment to the arrival of an older child in the family. Yet in many other situations, the new child feels forever challenged and never finds a place in the family, and the now younger child feels forever dethroned and at war in the family.

Two unrelated children at once

Some parents ask about adopting two unrelated children at one time. This practice, and especially adopting children who are close in age, is almost always discouraged. These parents might consider that for financial reasons this would be the best deal for them, but historically it has not worked well and has resulted in great difficulties for many children. Children who have not lived together before they arrive in an adoptive family will tend to vie for position forever within that adoptive family. Too often children are so different from each other and their adjustment within the family is so differentiated that, without the genetic tie, one of the children may not be accepted within the family. It is much easier for kids who come from the same birth family to adjust to the new adoptive family. They tend to support and look out for one another. In some cases, this principle can be extended to two children who have grown up together since birth in an orphanage setting.

The favored "arrival"

Children often ask for a little brother or little sister. The request comes from having observed other families and seeing the playful interaction and companionship among them. We know, however, that in many families the extra attention paid to the "baby" in the family often causes jealousy soon after the child's arrival, whether there was lengthy preparation for the new arrival or not. In short, the baby is not yet the playmate the older sibling expected and so there is disappointment exhibited as jealousy, frustration, recklessness, or even anger. The expectation is for a "ready-made" playmate, able to do more than babies, yet young enough and new enough so that the older child can keep charge and gradually share the toys. Or, they are so distant in age that they do not compete with one another. Also, when older children are adopted, their personalities are already well formed, and they may be conceived as "so different" that they never form a close relationship with younger siblings in the family. Parents need to be open and flexible and understand that this can happen just as it might in a newly formed step family.

Exercise: Our Home

Obviously, the many variables of numbers, ages, first or not first, and personalities of the children and parents will make for many combinations. To think ahead to your "ideal" family makeup, complete this drawing exercise. Within the space, sketch out a floor plan of your house (or dream house), noting the locations of bedrooms, who sleeps where, playroom, family room, offices. Especially note where people tend to gather. Then with a different color pen or pencil, proceed to a date in the future, perhaps six months after the arrival of your adopted child, and place family members inside your play house. Show the changes you expect may have been made.

Descriptions

Our family members in _____ (a chosen for future date, e.g., in 5-10 years).

_____

_____

_____

_____

Father (describe temperament)

_____

_____

_____

_____

Mother (describe temperament)

_____

_____

_____

_____

First child (adopted) (sex) (age) (temperament and characteristics)

_____
_____
_____
_____

Second child (adopted) (sex) (age) (temperament and characterisics)

_____
_____
_____
_____

Continue as far as you wish.

_____
_____
_____
_____
_____

Questions

1. On what did you base your description of your family in the future?

_____
_____
_____
_____

2. How do you think your children will get along? How do you envision them as teenagers?

_____

_____

_____

_____

_____

3. What if their temperaments and interests are very different from others in the family?

_____

_____

_____

_____

_____

4. Do you foresee that you will have to do some extra work in your family on the image of the male/female? What?

_____

_____

_____

_____

_____

5. Give an example of the kind of "work" you plan to do on your image as an international family.

_____

_____

_____

_____

_____

17
. . . .

When They Fight, Test, and Act Out

When adoptive parents receive a very young infant, they know and expect some difficult "first-times": the first time she gets sick, the first time I cannot comfort him, the first time he cries all night long.

These will happen within the first few months of an adoption; they are difficult, but parents are prepared because these behaviors and events appear to be very "normal."

Coping with unexpected behavior

Parents who adopt older children may intellectually know about but somehow don't expect the following behaviors:

- A child destroys something on purpose.

- A child uses physical force to harm a sibling, parent or pet.

- A child throws up food on purpose, regresses to bed-wetting, urinates on the floor, or smears feces on the wall.

- A child forces sexual play on a school mate or playmate.

- A child tries to set fire to something.

- A child points a knife and threatens.

- A child becomes so clingy that the adoptive parent feels the need to get away.

- A child makes inappropriate sexual advances to a parent or a sibling.

These behaviors may not happen right away, they may not all happen or they may never happen with your child. The point of this exercise and this workbook is not to alarm but to prepare. The question is not whether these behaviors might occur, but, "What would I do and how would we react if these behaviors did occur?"

Exercise

On the right are some possible reasons, causes and background on older adoptive children and what might prompt reactive or regressive behaviors. These have all been taken from real-life examples.

Your task is to correlate the causes with the possible behaviors. Draw lines across the columns. Many behaviors will have more than one possible cause. There are no exact right or wrong answers. Use the exercise as a base for discussion rather than a search for the answers.

Behaviors

- Destruction of house property
- Purposeful destruction or loss of own toys, clothes, etc.
- Running away or hiding
- Hiding or stealing another's things
- Physical force against a parent
- Physical force against a sibling
- Physical force against a playmate
- Physical force against another adult in charge, i.e., teacher, babysitter, coach
- Forced sexual play
- Threatens or attempts to use a knife or harmful instrument on self
- Threatens or attempts to use a knife or harmful instrument on others
- Setting fires
- Clingy, possessive behavior
- Torturing a family pet
- Regressive bladder or sphincter control
- Smears feces, mud, purposely dirties
- Urinates on wall of bedroom
- Is sad, withdrawn
- Will not eat
- Cries continuously and cannot be consoled

Causes

- My child witnessed this behavior in a previous living situation.
- My child was a victim of this behavior by others in previous living situations.
- At first everything here was a Disney World, but now he/she misses the old and former life and is angered that it was taken away.
- Something here reminds my child of what he/she had in his/her former life and lost (a favorite toy, activity, person).
- My child is on overload for learning so many new things.
- My child is frustrated because his/her language no longer works in this country.
- My child fears that because he/she got "taken away" before, it might happen again.
- My child thinks that if he misbehaves, he'll be sent back to the familiar surroundings he misses.
- My child feels out of control now because everyone has always told him what to do.
- My child feels so different from every one else.

Questions

How will we react in any of the above situations? (How might we have reacted before doing this exercise, when we were totally unprepared for what might occur?)

_____

_____

_____

_____

_____

_____

How will we know when to seek professional help? (Discuss a parallel situation: How would we go about seeking help if we suspected that our child had a vision or hearing problem?)

_____

_____

_____

_____

_____

What should we ask the professional regarding his/her sensitivity and experience with international adopted children? How might we find such a person?

_____

_____

_____

_____

_____

_____

Parent readiness

Parents often underestimate the life skills that they have acquired. They tend to think that parenting requires unique skills that they certainly do not have because they are not parents yet. However, look at the following list and check the skills you think you already have, but learned from life in general. Each of these skills are extremely applicable to parenting:

- working as a team
- knowing to ask for help
- managing stress
- intelligence/ seeing the whole picture
- honesty/ directness
- humor/patience
- optimism/hope
- taking one day at a time
- seeing others as unique and changing
- willing to admit mistakes and try again
- warmth and affection
- affirming/finding something good in others

Additional skills I want to develop:

_____

_____

_____

_____

_____

_____

_____

_____

_____

_____

Talking with a child after a major incident

Parents of a 2-year-old soon learn that when their child is in the throes of a temper tantrum, talk does not often help, and the best strategy is to let the tantrum run its course. Parents also know by instinct that the learning time comes later, when talking and explaining can help the child modify his behavior for the next time.

Adoptive parents who know some particularly negative facts about their child (such as early abuse or neglect) often wonder when and if these facts should be introduced.

Because the general rule is "when helpful and appropriate to the child's understanding," this needs practice. It is also helpful to explain the child's past in a way that he/she can understand and accept it, just as parents explain sex to their children at the child's level of understanding. Here are some examples to practice.

1. A parent of a 7-year-old knows that her adopted son used to beg in the streets until age 3. The child is caught stealing in school. Practice how a mother-to-son conversation might go after the initial crisis is over.

   _____

   _____

   _____

2. A parent of a 5-year-old girl finds that his daughter is losing almost all her toys, mittens, clothes in kindergarten due to lack of care for them. The parent knows that his daughter lived the first three years of her life with nothing to call her own. Practice how the conversation might go or what the parent might do.

   _____

   _____

   _____

Discuss

Are there some pieces of a child's history you consider should never be shared?

_____

_____

_____

_____

_____

What if knowing this information might help the child understand herself/himself and the behaviors?

_____

_____

_____

_____

_____

What might happen if, as a young adult, your son/daughter learned this information and also learned that you, the adoptive parent, had concealed it?

_____

_____

_____

_____

Mixed feelings

Sometimes children fight, test, and act out because of the confusion they sense inside themselves. As newly adopted children, they experience a barrage of mixed and often conflicting feelings. There is excitement and sadness all at once. They may experience fear or panic at the same time they sense the urge to try everything new. They may feel helpless or powerless because they have no familiar language and at the same time feel a sense of hope and comfort. They may feel anger and relief at the same time. Because of this phenomenon of "mixed feelings," we can expect behaviors that appear odd and need a lot of second guessing on the part of the parents.

Exercise

Here are some signs and symptoms of mixed feelings among children. Try to continue the list and then discuss how you might help as parents.

- A child playing with a playmate calmly, who suddenly turns on him/her.

- A child having fun in the midst of a theme park, who suddenly starts to scream at the sight of something.

- A child who begins to laugh when seeing someone get hurt.

18

• • • • • • • • • • • • • • • •

Openness in International Adoption and Birth Families Revisited

In countries where child welfare agencies and authorities have counseled the birth family, communication between the adoptive family and birth parents may be permitted and encouraged. It is a generally accepted belief in adoption today that the more an adopted child and birth parents avoid secrets and maintain open communication, the better the child's adjustment. This was not always so in the United States and is still not widely accepted in other countries. Where it is, we feel fortunate for the children and all parties involved.

Even when a child comes from an orphanage as legally "abandoned," the term does not mean that the child was left in

the middle of "nowhere" or that no one knows anything about anyone connected to the child. It usually means that the birth parents did not formally relinquish the child to the orphanage or to the social service agency. Information may be available.

In their preparation stages, adoptive parents often do not think about obtaining further information during their travel to adopt, or about meeting birth or foster families. They may not think ahead to a time in their child's life when a reconnection with the birth family might be healing or helpful. For some adopted children, knowing their birth parents or knowing about them is not critical to their identity. To many children it is.

The most common question categories older adopted children have for their birth parents (and wish you had found out for them...or may want to know soon)

- Why did you "give me up"?
- Did you love me when you found out you were pregnant? What was it like when you were pregnant with me? Who helped you? Were you alone or with my birth father? Where did you live? What were you doing to earn a living?
- What was it like when you delivered me? Where were you? Who was with you? Did you hold me when I was born? Did you breastfeed me? How long was I with you?
- Did you name me? Why did you choose the name? Who was I named after?
- What was it like the day you "gave me up"? Who was there? Was it hard?
- Do you think about me often? Do you remember my birthday?
- Do I have brothers and sisters? Who are they? Were they adopted? Where are they? What do they look like? What are they doing? Did you love them more than me?

Exercise

The following points help you as pre-adoptive parents think through the process of an open adoption before you choose a country, receive a child referral or travel to the country. You will have some choices and decisions to make along the way:

- You might decide to choose a country where openness is a somewhat common practice, knowing that for the most part it varies by the wishes of each set of birth parents.
- You might be asked in some situations to meet the birth parents or to be "matched" with birth parents in international countries who have specific requests.

- You may be able to request to meet the birth mother/father as you travel to the country to adopt.
- You may be receiving communications by e-mail, letter, and/or visits with the birth parents in years to come.

We will concentrate on meeting a birth parent or communicating with birth parents by e-mail, letter or visits, as the first two will depend upon your adoption agency and the country programs they have set up for adoption.

(Note: In the case of abusive birth parents, there are obvious modifications of this principle.)

Meeting birth parents in another country

You are scheduled to meet the birth parents (or possibly the long-term foster parents) while in your child's country for the adoption.

To set this in a parallel situation, think back to a first meeting that you set up to introduce a significant other to your own parents. Get a situation in mind and then talk about these statements:

- I had some time to think about it and I talked to my parents ahead of time and told them what to expect, and how I felt about this person.

- I gave my parents some hints about how I'd like them, as parents, to react to or treat my guest.

- I, nevertheless, worried about...

- I wanted everything to go well; I had a lot invested in this.

- I knew my parents would be surprised by...

- I had a feeling my parents would react to...

- The things I hadn't planned on were...

Now let's bring this to the situation of meeting your child's birth parents in country:

- You will most likely have little or no control over setting up the meeting. Your country representative will be arranging it at the very last minute and may forget the little details!

- With your best laid plans, the meeting and its trimmings (like videotaping it, taking pictures, giving a gift) may go well ☐ or not. Example: One family reported they met their Guatemalan birth mother as they jumped into the representative's car in the midst of rush hour traffic to find her stuffed in the rear seat facing backwards!

- As much as you would like to speak directly and express your feelings, joys, and sympathies all at once, you will most likely have to work through an interpreter. This is awkward in itself because you may not know whose face to look at as you speak.

There are some cultural differences that come into play here. For an exercise in becoming acquainted with them, try numbering this list of 10 items in what you think is their order of importance.

___ In their eyes, we're rich, they're poor, and this is going to be difficult. They may think we are a source of money for them for the rest of their lives.

___ They're wondering why so many U.S. families can't have children and come to their country to adopt.

___ In their families, "giving away" a child is something to hide. They will be worried about keeping this a secret.

___ They may think from TV that people from the United States often abuse children or don't raise them properly. Will they think of us as part of this stereotype?

___ They may think from TV that American kids are spoiled. Will they think we will follow this stereotype?

___ We'll be looking at them to see how tall and handsome our child might be when she or he grows up. This will feel quite awkward.

___ How will they feel if we ask them if there are any genetic diseases in their background, or should we even ask this?

___ Will we cry and be so overwhelmed with emotion that we will not present ourselves the way we had hoped? Or will we be so afraid we won't show any emotion?

___ Will the birth parents change their minds and try to reverse the adoption once they meet us and realize the child is truly leaving?

___ What if the parents are truly different than what we expected, like unable to speak, function, or communicate in any way?

Exploring cultural differences

One of the great differences between open U.S. adoptions and open international adoptions is cultural and locational ignorance. We simply do not know another culture because we have not lived it. We do not have an image of PLACE because we have most likely not been to the city of our child's birth. In the United States, if you are about to be matched with birth parents who say they live in an apartment in such-and-such a city, you can put an image in your head. Apartment: entryway, street scenes, buses, cars, local fast food places, etc.

Look at the photos on this page. Imagine where your child's birth parents live.

Go ahead, sketch some furniture in the living space...

Communicating by e-mail, letters, and visits with the birth parents in the years to come

Even though social circumstances in your child's country of birth may not include the practice of meeting the child's birth parents or even talking to the persons at the orphanage who took the child in, you may consider writing a letter, stating your desire to be open to future communication once your child is old enough to understand the concept of adoption.

In this letter you can also state that you wish a file on your family be left at the orphanage with your local U.S. agency's return address, write an agreement that you will send pictures and a letter each year and that you are open to having that orphanage or agency share them with a birth parent who might return and ask about the child she or he placed for adoption. The letter can include that you would be very open to receiving letters and photos from the birth parents and are willing to pay for the postage.

Using your agency's address rather than your own is often more acceptable to the authorities and will safeguard you against any complications of birth parents requesting money from you or overstepping boundaries.

Questions families frequently ask about international openness

What will my meeting with a birth parent be like?
Who will be there?

Adoptive families who have met their child's birth parent(s) in country describe it as an amazing experience full of awe and mixed emotions. You may feel overwhelmed by the magnitude of the experience and the emotions that the birth parent(s) is experiencing.

Your agency may be able to provide you with a list of possible questions to ask the birth parent; however, the most important part of this meeting is just to establish a connection. Because of the language barrier, you may find that most of the communication happens through nonverbal interaction. Adoptive families that have been through this experience often well up with emotion when they recall what it was like to meet the birth mother at a time when she could see them and the child together. You may wish to videotape parts or the entire meeting as many families find it difficult to describe later on.

In addition to a translator, you will most likely have agency representatives or a facilitator present during the meeting. These people are there to support you during this time.

What will our child's parents want to know about us and is it okay to bring gifts for them?

They will most likely want to know what their child's new life is going to be like. Where will they be living? What will their room look like? Who else is in your family? You may wish to bring a small photo album for them with pictures that answer these questions. They may also wish to know what you are going to name your child and if you will be keeping any part of his birth name. Many families also bring a small piece of jewelry such as a necklace with the child's birthstone. One family drew a map of the United States during the meeting in order to give the birth mother a concept of where their child will be growing up.

What type of ongoing contact do people generally have?

Following an initial meeting, contact is generally maintained through pictures and letters sent through the agency. Although many young Koreans have access to e-mail and know some English, it is strongly encouraged that contact continue through the agency until a relationship has been established between all of the parties and everyone is comfortable with the level of openness. Often families will find that communication is fairly one-sided. You may send letters and pictures and not receive anything from the birth family. Part of this is due to the culture ⬜ for example, Korea is not a letter writing society. Historically letters were reserved for hallmark occasions such as births, weddings, and deaths. When families do receive letters or "notes" from birth families, they may be surprised by how short they are.

Communication may also be one-sided in Guatemala. Many birth parents do not read or write and may have to have letters read for them. They most likely won't have pictures to send you, access to a phone, or access to e-mail. They may live in a mountain village at least a day's journey from where the facilitator who helped them lives. This may make it difficult for them to get regular correspondence.

Although the communication may be one-sided for many years, you are building a bridge for your child to their birth family. This will make it easier for your child to establish contact with birth family members when they are older. It is an investment in their future relationships with birth family members that your child will appreciate you making. Whether or not they wish to have contact in the future, they will know the effort you made at making that connection.

While most adoptive families see the benefits of writing their child's birth family, many find it hard to do so as time goes on. One adoptive mother said that it is hard to write because the happiness you have gained through your child corresponds with this person's pain and loss. Another adoptive family said that they have had difficulty choosing pictures to send to their child's birth mother because they are afraid if their daughter looks too happy the birth mother will regret her decision and feel more pain over it. Many families find that once their child joins their family their lives get very busy and it is easy to forget, especially if the relationship is one-sided at first. These are all difficult aspects of a new relationship that may feel unlike any other relationship you have ever had.

Regardless, we encourage families to maintain contact with birth families, especially if you made an agreement with them to do so. You will find that the investment in your child's future is well worth the cost of your time. We encourage you to keep copies of the letters and pictures that you send so that your child can be familiar with the communication that has been sent to birth family members.

What do I do if my child's birth family asks for money?

In other cultures it is more common for extended family members to provide financial support for each other. By adopting one of their family members, birth relatives may come to view you as an extended part of their family. This may mean that they feel comfortable coming to you with financial requests.

They may also have a distorted view of how much money you have. For this reason, we encourage communication after the adoption to go through the facilitator in country and your agency here. If a request for financial aid is received, the agency will pass this information on to you. There have been times when adoptive families have sent financial assistance. For instance, one birth mother's home was burnt down by the birth father. Another birth mother wanted to have a tubal ligation. Other birth mothers have needed assistance for medical treatment. In addition to the support you may send, your agency may have a fund for these types of situations.

Will I be setting my child up to feel a responsibility for his/her birth family members in the future?

The truth is, many adopted children feel a responsibility for birth family members whether or not there has been contact. You cannot prevent your child from feeling this sense of responsibility. It is a normal feeling, particularly for children who have been adopted internationally. Trying to protect your children from this feeling may only make it worse.

What is the hardest part about international openness?

When you meet your child's birth parent(s), you will most likely find yourself wondering what he or she is thinking about this adoption. Are they comfortable with the adoption plan? Open adoptions, whether international or domestic, always raise adoptive families' awareness of how difficult and painful it is for birth parents to make an adoption decision.

You will become much more aware of how your tremendous gain is somebody else's deep loss. You may find yourself wondering how your child's birth mother is dealing with the loss. Does she have anyone she can talk to about it? Will this be a secret she has to guard from her family, children and community? Who can she tell about her meeting with you? While you may be leaving this meeting with your spouse and child, you may wonder if she has anyone to go home to. Undoubtedly this will create a dichotomy of feelings for you that can be quite bittersweet.

There is also an internal struggle for many adoptive families who want to know as much as possible about their child's birth relatives but also want to respect the culture of secrecy within which most international birth parents live. You may have to get comfortable with not having a lot of answers. In fact, meeting your child's birth parent(s) will most likely raise *more* questions than answers for you!

At what point do you involve the children in the communication?

We encourage families to involve their children in the communication as early as possible. At first this may mean sending some of your child's art or an imprint of their hand. As they get older they may like to help select which pictures get sent and eventually they may wish to write letters themselves.

Involving your child in the communication sends a positive message to birth parent(s) and also tells your child that this relationship is theirs to foster as they wish and are able to do. Developing this relationship will make it that much easier for you and your child if your child decides to travel back to meet birth family members in the future.

19

Talking About Adoption

There will be key moments in your child's life when these memories, whole or partial, will come back or will be felt in some way. It is at this time that your child will seek to clarify those experiences, just as birth children will ask to see their baby pictures, their baby book, and other mementos.

Any child who has spent the first few years of life with a birth family, in an orphanage, or with a foster family will have a verbal or pre-verbal memory (or a temporarily blocked memory) of the persons who cared for him or her. These memories might include any of the following:

- soothing and comforting (or the opposite in abuse and neglect)

- feeding

- changing diapers

- bathing

- holding, cuddling

- saying "no" or disciplining

- celebrating or delighting in something

Exercise

Losing a native language often means also losing memories. Your child may not be able to recreate or remember early childhood experiences in the usual way. We can, by remembering things from our past, think of ways to help.

What items, photos, memories do you still have and cherish from your earliest years of childhood?

_____

_____

_____

_____

_____

_____

What are some of the questions you asked your parents about your infancy and childhood, and why were they important to you?

_____

_____

_____

_____

_____

How might your identity have been affected if you never saw your birth parents, never knew your name, and knew nothing of your genetic or medical history?

_____

_____

_____

_____

_____

Discussion

These are some issues and questions to think about and be prepared to answer:

What would I say to my child if he asked whether his adoptive parent(s) would ever do a thing like "give me away"?

_____

_____

_____

_____

_____

_____

Is poverty always a good way to "explain" birth parents' motives in adoption?

_____

_____

_____

_____

_____

What would I say to my child if she expressed dislike or hatred for her birth parents / for her people / for her country?

_____

_____

_____

_____

_____

Is it possible a child would feel guilty for having left her birth parents behind? Explain.

_____

_____

_____

_____

_____

What are some other possible questions from adopted teens in search of their identities and sense of self-worth in life?

_____

_____

_____

_____

_____

When a child is constantly given messages that he is "lucky" to have been adopted (rescued), what might result?

_____

_____

_____

_____

_____

If a child expresses thoughts that he probably would have been better off if he had stayed in his country, what might this indicate? How should an adoptive parent answer?

_____

_____

_____

_____

_____

Some adoptive parents seek to clarify their child's questions and inquiries by making a trip back to the child's country-of-origin, or finding a pen-pal from that country, participating in some mission or charity in the country, giving school reports or taking part in projects on that country or on adoption. They may start a savings account for their young adult's own future trip back to the country, or join an agency's or group's adoption tour back to the country. Any or all of these ideas may be worthwhile, and you will know what is right for your child as his or her search for identity progresses.

For now, your task as an adoptive parent is to prepare for the future. For those parents who do not have information about their child's background or the opportunity for openness in their adoption, we offer a substitute called:

MY JOURNEY HOME

The task is to do a kind of baby book or a life book for your child. We include here the possible text and ideas for photos or articles you might include in the book:

I.   This is a story about you (photo). It tells how you came with your parents from a land called _____ to the United States.

II. Your native country is _____ (map). People in _____ have their own special way of life. They speak their own language, which when written looks like this:

_____

_____

_____

When we went to _____ to get you, the daily newspaper's front page looked like this on your adoption day. (Newspaper articles, ads, cultural events, etc.)

III. _____ has its own cultural dance, music, art, and architecture. Here are post cards (photos) of what impressed us.

IV. _____ sometimes dress in traditional costume. We bought you one of these outfits to give to you as you grew up so that you would remember the importance of your people and the meaning of this clothing: (Photograph or explanation)

V. The capital city _____ looks like this and has _____ people. The country is known for its _____.

VI. Once upon a time in this special land called _____ a mother had a little baby — YOU. You were a happy baby and your mother loved you very much. But life was not easy for your mother/father because:

_____

_____

_____

_____

_____

_____

And for this reason you were brought to_____.

We have a picture of where you were; we saw it, and we talked with the people who cared for you.

The day we first met you, you were in _____
dressed like _____
brought to us by _____
from the room where you had been _____
You looked at us and *(continue the story using concrete descriptions of space, place, time sequence)*

_____
_____
_____
_____
_____
_____
_____
_____
_____
_____

VII. And finally the day arrived when you were ready to come home with us to the United States. The plane was _____
and the ride took _____
and when we arrived you _____
We brought you home to your first night with us in the home and room we had prepared for you: (photo)

VIII. Those first weeks at home with us were ones of _____
_____
You played mostly with _____
You loved to eat _____
We took you to _____
_____
_____

IX. Your first English words were _____

_____

Your first new friend was _____

Your first and most special toy was _____

Your favorite place to go was _____

Your first disappointment was

_____

_____

_____

_____

Your first great achievement in school was

_____

_____

_____

_____

X. Reading this, there are probably lots of things we forgot to fill in. But they are still all there in our memories, so ask your questions here:

_____

_____

_____

_____

(Note: Sometimes it is easier if you ask a child specific questions like: "Do you ever wonder if your birth parents had other children? " "Do you ever think about going back to India?)

Talking about adoption

As with many concept words, children grow up hearing but not understanding the word "adoption" or the phrase "you were adopted." International children observe that they look different from others and from their parents early in life and so often hear phrases such as "You were adopted," "Your birth parents...," and "Your adoptive parents..." This does not mean children understand, but they are at least familiar with the vocabulary as youngsters.

Secrecy about adoption, or neglect in answering a child's questions, is considered damaging and harmful, and yet it is difficult for adoptive parents to share a lot because they have little to share. In many countries, birth mothers keep their pregnancies a secret from the birth father or from their own families, and adoption personnel often wish to keep secret the identity and details about a child's birth parents. Children, as they grow up and ask questions about the past, can sense the hesitation and  the anxiety expressed in their parents' answers. It is even more difficult when adoptive parents know information they consider damaging to tell a child (for example, the child is a product of rape or a birth parent was in jail for murdering the other).

Discussion

Consider the following:

What is the potential harm in sharing difficult information with your child?

_____

_____

_____

_____

At what age might this change?_____

Can too much openness or candor leave my child vulnerable?

_____

_____

_____

Can too much secrecy leave my child isolated?

_____

_____

_____

Is there likely to be information in my child's orphanage or court record that will surprise or hurt her if she searches it out later in life?

_____

_____

_____

What if my child shows a decided disinterest in his roots? Does this mean I have done something wrong?

_____

_____

_____

20
· · · · · · · · · · · · · · · ·

An International Family

This project focuses on you, the parents in an international family, on your promise to the country's adoption personnel to continue and value your child's heritage, on your child's new and old language, and on your ties to the "causes" and social welfare needs in your child's birth country.

There are many challenges in raising an international family, and although they do not press in on you immediately, we mention them in this chapter.

Children of color

There is a prevalent belief in many parts of the U.S. that you cannot teach a child of color how to cope in a white world. You need to find someone else to help. If not, at age 20, or whenever your child moves into adulthood, he will wonder where he really belongs. All through her life, others may expect your child to be different because she appears different. It is important to consider how to help your child cope as he looks in the mirror and sees his color as "white inside" and "dark outside."

Continuing your child's heritage

Often the question arises, "Why should I continue to teach my child the heritage of his birth country?" Many parents consider that their children are having a "hard enough" time assimilating all that the U.S. means without having to "keep up" on India or Colombia or wherever. The answer is, "This is who your child is..." as normally as you would want to continue to let your child draw or sing or dance if that was her special talent when she arrived, then just as normally would you continue her culture. If you cut it off, you would be cutting off a part of her. It's fine in theory to continue the culture, but what about practice?

Culture, in this context, becomes more a verb than a noun, just as draw, sing, or dance are verbs. Your children are not just Russian or Vietnamese because they may "look" that way, but because they have been acting and living that way before they came to you.

Expectations that come from cultural norms

Below is a mix of customs and expectations of many different countries. Read them and then create your own list according to what you know about your child's country and what you wish to continue in your family.

1. Receive and give gifts on the date of the visit of the Magi (always January 6).
2. Sleep on the floor or in bed with parents or siblings.
3. Greet people by a kiss on both cheeks, but not an embrace or hug or hand shake.
4. Eat meals in silence, eating with fingers, cleaning plates with a piece of bread.
5. Continue to speak the native language, sing native songs, recite poems, riddles, etc.
6. Spend Sundays visiting with relatives and friends, have huge gatherings at your house.
7. Walk places, never in a hurry, arriving late or not always arriving or expecting others to keep appointments, and arrive unannounced.
8. Give away your toys and clothes to anyone who says they like them. Come home with other people's things.
9. Talk to someone "in their face" (being physically very close during communication), talk loudly, and talk to elders with downcast eyes.
10. Celebrate a birthday by throwing a surprise bucket of water on the celebrant.

11. Celebrate New Year's/Christmas/birthdays with firecrackers but not with gifts.

12. Become aggressive (macho) rather than express frustration with words or tears.

13. Remain passive during an attack on ego or self.

14. Hide rather than express wants/feelings.

15. Have certain foods as celebration, certain foods as daily fare, have very spicy or very sweet food, etc.

16. Remember and emulate the heroes of the country.

17. Look up to or down at certain segments of the family unit/society.

18. Expect that education/work/marriage/family life will be...

Our list of country customs and expectations

Write below ideas about which customs from your child's country you will continue and how you will carry them on.

_____

_____

_____

_____

_____

_____

_____

_____

_____

_____

_____

_____

_____

_____

_____

Discussion

As you completed the previous exercise, undoubtedly you were faced with the question of how your child can adapt to his new culture and still remember and honor where he came from. Complete the following sentence, and then share your answer with someone else:

I think that living with two (or more) cultures in our family will be

_____

_____

_____

because

_____

_____

What are some possible "negatives" my child might hear about his/her native country (e.g., drugs, Communism, poverty, etc.) and how will I treat these?

_____

_____

_____

_____

How can I be sure not to over-compensate or over-emphasize the positive aspects of my child's culture (will my child sense I am doing this on purpose to cover up something)?

_____

_____

_____

_____

When people ask about our adopted child in his/her presence, what should we say and how will what we say be interpreted by our child? Try out different scenarios using these and other insensitive questions.

- "Your child must be adopted. Where from?"
- "Do they have a lot of kids for adoption there?"
- "Are all the kids this color?"
- "Do you know why he was given up for adoption?"

Language Adaptation

Here are the most common counsels given by language teachers for children who need to adapt to a new language. First, see if you agree with them, then rewrite and personalize them for your family and your child's age.

1. Encourage but do not demand speech upon his/her arrival. Do not begin some kind of sign language unless it is accompanied by words.
2. Walk around the house several times a week naming several objects.
3. Use familiar words with much repetition and in several ways. For example, try "Get the ball," "Ivan has the ball," "You've got the ball," "Let's throw the ball."
4. Expose your child to other children as role models. This will be less threatening and the natural desire to play will take over the fear of language that happens in the presence of adults only.
5. Use a mirror with you and your child watching how the sounds "look." Good language videos also give this closeup look of how the mouth is formed and individual sounds are made. Isolate the sounds your child has trouble with.
6. Repeat an incorrect word correctly and make a game with your child of trying it again (but do not prolong or overdo this technique).
7. Do not change your grammatical structure (for example, "Go bed!") because you think it will be easier. (Whether to omit a lot of slang or not is debatable in teaching a 4-year-old or older child a new language. Some fear that the child may then never learn to distinguish between slang and non-slang.)

8. Continue to use or learn to use the child's favorite words in his native language. Mixing them with English, as long as they are not always substituted for words such as mom, dad, foods, toys, etc., will not confuse or hinder the child's language development. Most parents consider the use of their own mixture of native/new words to be something that helps them bond with a child.

9. Continue to expose your child to native speakers from his/her country or continue phone calls to people he/she knows in the country, all other factors being positive. Learn and use some of his/her language.

10. Do not lament your child's loss of a previous language or overly celebrate mastery of the new language to him/her.

11. Know that a normal stage for a child is to reject the former language and want to be "totally American."

Exercise:

Write here your first month's plan for helping your child adapt to her new language.

_____

_____

_____

Write here what celebrations, foods, rituals, etc. you plan to continue for your child at this point:

_____

_____

_____

Write what items of art, souvenir, and picture books you presently plan to purchase for your child's room, family use, etc.:

_____

_____

21
• • • • • • • • • • • • •

Resources

We are happy to recommend resources that we feel are especially beneficial to families and these will be described under the chapter headings where they seem appropriate. However, because of the constantly changing resources, and because we believe it is very important for you, as an adoptive family, to identify resources that are particularly relevant for you and within your community, we also ask you to do some homework in finding and identifying resources that are your own. To the extent that you involve yourself and invest in this process, this section will have more value to you. It can be a place that you look back to, after your child has arrived, to look for resources that are needed at that time.

In your preparation for adoption, we strongly recommend that you join a parent support group either through your agency, your city/state, or through the internet. Other parents can often fill in details from their experiences that agencies may not have time to do. We add the caution that no two adoptions will ever be the same in their process, and so a direct comparison between another

parent's adoption and yours may be futile. There will, however, be many, many areas of helpful advice from other parents.

Chapter 1: The Image of Our Child

In thinking about this child who will become a part of your family, have you thought about the name for the child? In general, it is felt that children who are old enough to recognize their name do best if their name is retained. However, many families use the child's original name in combination with a new name given by the family. While waiting for your child, identify resources that will help you find culturally appropriate names for the child you expect.

Notes_____
_____
_____
_____

Chapter 2: Adoption: Gains and Losses

Many families who are in the process of adopting have reached this place in their lives because they've experienced infertility. Many families have already involved themselves in the national organization RESOLVE, which is a support and education group for families who are experiencing infertility. If you have not already used this resource, find a local chapter of RESOLVE and attend a meeting. (Visit www.resolve.org)

In addition, there are other steps you can take to prepare yourself to understand the losses that all members of the triad (you, your child, your child's birth parents) feel in adoption. Look for a panel in your community where birth parents speak about their experience in making an adoption plan for their child. Look for a panel where adopted persons speak about their experience growing up in a family to which they came by adoption. If possible, find some cultural places or different neighborhoods where you clearly do not belong and generally do not go, and visit those places, and experience what it's like to be in situations in which you are unfamiliar and do not necessarily know the rules for behavior.

There are several excellent books available that address losses and gains. *Adopting After Infertility* by Patricia Johnston (www.perspectivespress.com) is an excellent book for you to use as a resource. Chapter 3 of the book deals with what you may have been through in your infertility process and how that may affect your adoption. *Helping Children Cope with Separation and Loss*, by Claudia Jewett, is an excellent resource that will help you find the words to explain your child's history.

Notes _____

_____

_____

_____

Chapter 3: The Sounds of Early Life

In order to experience and have ready sounds that will be familiar to your child from the child's own culture, investigate sources for audio tapes from the child's country of origin. Check with local bookstores and your local library where audio tapes may be rented. Borrow some music or language tapes from people originally from your child's country. If your child is older and has learned the language of his country, look for resources to learn the child's language. Even a few simple phrases and words can be very helpful in the early weeks of placement. In addition, if your child is older and speaking the language of his country, it may be appropriate to find a translator who speaks the child's language and can at least temporarily help you and your child understand one another better, until the child's English is more established. Obvious places to look for both of these last two items would be colleges and universities in your area, or international institutes that offer language classes and translating. In larger cities, hospitals may offer translators' services, which can be very helpful for medical visits early on.

Notes

_____

_____

_____

_____

Chapter 4: Food and All That It Means

In order to understand foods from your child's culture, visit restaurants in your area that specialize in cuisine from your child's country. This will give you insights into the smells and look of the food, as well as its texture and taste. The restaurant may also play music from the child's country or have entertainment that gives a cultural aspect. Further, you may hear the child's language spoken, and meet people from the child's country. In addition, identify recipe books and grocery stores with food items from your child's country. Fix some of the dishes and experience the tastes of your child's culture. While you are waiting for your child to join your family, go through the grocery stores and look for foods that you would begin with, given what you understand about your child's age and present diet, and possible comfort level with foods. If your child may not have ever eaten crunchy, hard or spicy foods, make a list of "bland and smooth foods" to start. In case you might need them, look for articles and chapters in books on eating disorders in children and how children use foods in power struggles. Talk with your pediatrician and nutritionist about introducing foods and about food allergies.

Notes

_____

_____

_____

_____

Chapter 5: Beds and Sleep

In preparing to understand your child's needs around sleep, locate an adoptive family or two who have adopted from the country where you are planning to adopt. (Ask your adoption agency.) Talk with the family about the adjustment to sleeping that they experienced when their children were newly placed and how they dealt with any sleep problems that they encountered. _A Child's Journey Through Placement_, by Vera Fahlberg is an excellent book that addresses children's sleep problems, among many other topics. This book, although written for use in placing U.S. children, has many concrete suggestions and information that are very helpful in international placements as well. In addition, try to locate within your community a person from your child's country and ask how they slept in their country when they lived there and how children usually sleep. (Sleeping patterns are not the same in all cultures.) Look for and list (in case you need them later) articles or chapters of books on sleep disorders and nightmares and night terrors in children.

Notes _____

_____

_____

_____

Chapter 6: Child Development

While you are waiting, do some research into the many books available on child development. Read and identify a book or two that you think you will find particularly useful when your child arrives. It is important to understand normal child development as a basis for understanding where the likenesses and differences exist for children who are placed for adoption. This would also be a good time to contact your local school district and talk with personnel there regarding services that can be offered in early childhood education. Because your child may have developmental delays as a result of her placement while in her country of origin, you may want to investigate services provided by your local school district for children who have developmental delays. In addition, read about the mandated services available for children who need special education and understand what kinds of special education are offered for such children. If you believe your child may, because of the child's history and the information you've received, have a strong need for special education services, you may also want to identify a local advocacy group, who can help you to learn to advocate for your child within your school district.

If your child is already speaking his native language, identify resources related to teaching of English as a Second Language (ESL), and do some reading on the subject before the child arrives.

Notes _____

_____

_____

_____

Chapter 7: Preparing for the Abused Child

Inquire about therapists and counselors in your area who specialize in the problems of adopted children. It is important to find a therapist who is knowledgeable in the area of adoption, as adoption, and particularly adoption of a child who is older or from another country, presents additional dynamics that therapists need to be aware of and sensitive to. Identify several books about adoption in general that you will read. One of the best books available on the subject of parenting a child who has been sexually abused is *Adoption of a Sexually Abused Child,* edited by Joan McNamara and Bernard McNamara. Another book that many families have found helpful is *Raising Adopted Children* by Lois Melina. There are other excellent books available on the subject; explore your library and catalogues such as those offered by Tapestry Books (www.tapestrybooks.com), or read reviews of them on internet adoption sites.

Notes
_____
_____
_____
_____

Chapter 8: A Special Child

Research medical resource books that may be helpful in learning more about a medical condition your child may have. Some books that we recommend include *The Merck Manual of Diagnosis & Therapy* by David Halvery (Merck Sharp & Dohme Research Laboratories); *Stedman's Medical Dictionary* published by Williams & Wilkins; *Current Pediatric Diagnosis and Treatment*, which is a Lane Medical Book, edited by William Hay, et al. Again, additional resources are available; make yourselves familiar with the ones that you find more comfortable and that you think you may use.

It will be important for you to identify a pediatrician if you do not already have one. It is most useful to find a pediatrician who has some experience with children who have been adopted internationally. If you are working with a pediatrician who has no knowledge in this area, the pediatrician's reactions to certain information may be somewhat skewed or at least not quite the appropriate perspective.

Many clinics now specialize in working with children who come into families through international adoption. Up-to-date lists of clinics can be found through your agency or on adoption web sites, e.g. www.comeunity.com/adoption. Often families use the services of these clinics (which may be far away from them) to review the medical information and videos they receive on a child referred to them. The clinic doctors will review referral information, pictures and video tapes at a nominal cost, help you understand the terms and the orphanage care, and may be wonderful referral sources for additional medical resources you may need.

Often parents who live near these clinics bring their children for a complete assessment, following the child's arrival in this country. These clinics have experience in treating children for certain parasites, infections, rashes, etc. and can give advice for developmental therapies based on the statistics they keep and studies they do on the many children referred to them through international adoption.

Notes
_____
_____
_____
_____

Chapter 9: Transitions to Home

To help those parents who might receive a "well-trained" child, we suggest you spend some time in a toy store or at day care centers observing what toys children typically prefer at certain ages. Observe and try to gauge what toys a very neat and clean child might prefer over others. Then, just as you would with foods, use the toys your child will be attracted to first, and then gradually introduce others.

If you are adopting siblings and want to prepare for the child who will come as the "caretaker of the rest," you can use many of the same resources as "blended families" use. In general, many of the library and bookstore resources for parenting step-children and about blended families will have many principles that can be applied to adopted children.

Notes
_____
_____
_____
_____

Chapter 10: Enclosed in an Orphanage

Until recently, very little has been written on the subject of the adjustment of children who have been raised in orphanages into adoptive families, since until recently only small numbers of children were making that transition. As new adoption programs have opened, including programs in China and Eastern Europe, many more children who have been raised in orphanages are now being placed with adoptive families. Unfortunately, because of the newness of the situation, there is still a lack of well developed reading material available on this subject. Information is generally found in professional journals, or on the internet under the search names of "parenting post-institutionalized children." Another key word is "sensory integration."

In answering the questions in the chapter regarding orphanage care, it may be helpful for you to talk to families who have raised children and who can remember at what month of age their children played certain games to help them develop the usual skills and traits. Also, thinking of games to play with children like patty-cake and peek-a-boo will help you understand how children usually learn space, sequence, trust, perception, language, stories, and discrimination. If you found the exercises too difficult to answer, you may wish to do further reading on sensory integration. Books and videos are usually available on this subject from early childhood learning centers.

Notes
_____
_____
_____
_____

Chapter 11: Bonding to a Rejected Child

In the field of children's mental health, we continue to learn about attachment and about children who have problems with attachment. The newest thinking now believes that there are very few children who truly are not able to attach, but that many children have barriers to their attachment based upon their history. In the most extreme circumstances, for children who genuinely appear to have significant problems in the area of attachment, there are therapies available that are controversial, but successful for some children, to help foster attachment between the child and the adoptive parents.

In recent years, studies have been completed and experience has been gained and shared through the publication of many articles, reports and books. Visit www.tapestrybooks.com to order books of interest to you. You may find the following books helpful:

Holding Time, by Martha Welch, M.D.

Attaching in Adoption: Practical Tools for Today's Parents, by Deborah Gray

Notes

_____

_____

_____

Chapter 12: Separating from Caretakers

It will be useful in preparation to parent your child to talk with some adoptive parents who may have been present when their adopted child separated from the caregiver that he/she had always known.   Ask parents to talk about what they observed in this experience. It may also be helpful to visit daycare centers in your area and watch what happens when a child is dropped off by parents, particularly when a child is new to the daycare center.

Many local adoption agencies publish newsletters in which parents describe their first meeting with their child. Ask your adoption agency to give you some of these newsletters to read. Also, read child development books turning to the chapters or articles on "stranger anxiety," on preparing a child for the first day at school, etc., to get an idea of why a child finds separation so difficult.

Notes

_____

_____

_____

Chapter 13: Travel and Culture Shock

One of the best resources available to you in preparing to parent a child from another country and in preparing to travel are other parents who have adopted from that same country. It is best to talk specifically with families who have adopted from the same agency's program within the country you are using. These parents can have a wealth of information regarding their impressions of the country of their child's origin, the facility in which the child is cared for, travel experiences, and resources that they have identified. It is also important after you have talked with them to sort out what might have changed since they were there, remembering that international adoption changes are frequent and significant. (Ask about things like new orphanage doctors, caretakers, directors, practices, testing procedures, etc.)

In addition, check for reading materials regarding information on cultures in various countries, especially the books that are entitled, *Culture Shock--A Guide to Customs and Etiquette in _____.* These books are now available for most countries of adoption travel. Look for other books on customs in countries of travel, (e.g. the *Lonely Planet* series) even those directed towards business persons. They are all of value to prepare you for a very different experience as you travel to, wait in, and receive your child in a different culture.

Many adoptive parents use their computers to browse web sites on countries/travel and to read adoption bulletin boards and subscribe to groups for each country. Note that extremes are often expressed in these groups.

Notes_____
_____
_____
_____

Chapter 14: Home and Post-adoption

Prior to placement, you should be talking very clearly with your social worker regarding what services you can expect from your social worker and your agency. Ask about any post-finalization services that your agency may provide, and call other local adoption agencies to ask what post-adoption services they may offer, such as workshops for children or workshops for parents. Spend some time identifying a parents' support group that you think you would be comfortable with and attend a meeting, if that's possible, prior to placement. Identify newsletters that may be pertinent to your situation, such as *Parents of Children from India*, or *Parents of Children from Guatemala*. Think about whether you want a notice of arrival and your child's picture in an adoption newsletter. Think about what kind of announcements you plan to send and have fun preparing that announcement.

Designing Rituals of Adoption, by Mary Mason, is an excellent book that can help you to plan ceremonies or rituals around the child's entering the family by adoption.

Notes

Chapter 15: Preparing for Prejudice/ Being Different

It is also helpful during this time to read some books on child rearing around the world and how it differs from culture to culture. In preparing for parenting a child from a different racial and ethnic heritage, it is useful to read some books regarding racism and prejudice in our society. Consult the book lists from adoption magazines such as *Adoptive Familes* or *Adoption Today* and other resources for such books (www.rainbowkids.com has a large list). In addition, talk to parents who have traveled to the country you plan to travel to and talk with them about how they might have been rejected and what they wish they had done differently, both in preparing for their travel and while they were in the country.

In preparation for your child's arrival into your family, particularly if that child is coming from a different race or ethnic group, we suggest that you investigate schools in your area, play groups, and child care centers where there will be diversity and where your child may be comfortable.

Also, explore culture camps that may be offered in your state. Review lists of books for sale, to identify books that will be helpful for your child later when he/she feels different from you.

Notes

Chapter 16: Siblings in Adoption

When you are talking to families who have already adopted, spend some time talking about how their new child adapted to their existing family, particularly if there are other children already in the family. Talk about sibling rivalry and alliances which may change, with the introduction of a new child or children. Again, review books and magazine articles to find information on assisting siblings in developing a positive relationship. Vera Fahlberg's book, *A Child's Journey Through Placement,* includes material on this subject.

Notes _____

_____

_____

_____

Chapter 17: When They Fight

Explore materials on behavior management and discipline. Talk with your partner or family about styles of behavior management that you think will be comfortable for you. Find some books on genetics that relate to what portion of a child's personality may come from a genetic factor and what portion of a child's personality may be formed because of life experience. Talk to families, both adoptive families and others, about how they discipline children they are parenting.

Notes _____

_____

_____

_____

Chapter 18: Openness in International Adoption and Birth Families Revisited
Chapter 19: Talking About Adoption

We recommend *Talking With Young Children About Adoption,* by Mary Watkins and Susan Fischer, a book written to help families begin to talk with their child about his/her adoption history. Many parents feel that this is one of the most difficult areas in parenting an adoptive child, but they truly want to be able to do a good job of talking to the child about his/her history and have many concerns about doing it in the right way. Remember that you will have many opportunities to talk to your child about his history and birth family, and that this is a subject that you should introduce without waiting for a child's questions. Think about how you can begin accumulating things that will help your child understand his history, including pictures of places he has lived or special people in his life, pictures of birth parents, if available; mementos from the adoption experience. All of these will serve as excellent tools as you talk to your child over time about why an adoption plan was made and how she/he came to be in your family.

Notes
_____
_____
_____
_____

Chapter 20: An International Family

While waiting for your child, make a calendar of local cultural events that will help you to maintain your child's heritage.

Look in the children's section of your local library for books on your child's country, as these are often loaded with photos and often tell about the country with children specifically in mind.

Notes
_____
_____
_____
_____

Parent Groups

We strongly recommend that you join other groups of parents who have adopted or are adopting. Your local agency may provide information as a part of your adoption education, or you may need to search for these groups on your own. Web sites, adoption magazines and books are a good place to start.

Web Sites

Many parents use the internet as their first source of information about adoption agencies, and then to explore different programs and countries of adoption. They often join country-specific listservs and spend time corresponding with other parents who have chosen to adopt from the same country. Parents usually quickly learn that the advice and information they read on listservs may need to be taken with some caution: every adoption experience is different depending on factors such as the country, the adoption agency, the orphanage and country politics.

If you do choose to use the Web for information about adoption, we offer the following *advice:*

1. If you have not completed an adoption study and undergone your agency's preparation for an international adoption, you may wish to avoid web sites featuring photos of waiting children. These photos can pull your heartstrings and unless you are document-ready for an agency and a country (which can take up to 6 months), don't tease your emotions by becoming attached to a particular waiting child. Agencies and organizations put these children on sites for families who are ready, or close to ready, for a child referral.

2. Use the Web as a source of information to find a good adoption agency, to help you choose a country, to understand health issues of adoptive children; in short, for anything that expands upon what you have covered in this workbook.

3. If you choose to correspond on a listserv, please note that "net etiquette" almost always specifies that complaints made about adoption agencies or country agencies/officials remain *private* (that is, *off-list only*). These listservs are read internationally and may be misunderstood. Public complaints can seriously obstruct adoptions for other adoptive parents and may even cause a country to close its program of international adoption. Complaints are best taken up privately with an agency, or reported to the Better Business Bureau, any state's Adoption Services Unit or Attorney General, or a major body like the Joint Council of International Children's Services (www.jcics.org) or the National Council for Adoption (www.ncfa-usa.org).

The following web sites provide information about adoption:

International Adoption Agencies:

www.jcics.org provides a list of international adoption agencies belonging to the Joint Council of International Children's Services and provides useful information about international adoption.

www.yellow-pages.adoption.com provides a large list of international adoption agencies throughout the U.S.

www.adoptivefamilies.com provides a searchable data base of licensed adoption agencies throughout the U.S.

Adoption Books & Goods
www.tapestrybooks.com

www.perspectivespress.com

General Information for Adoptive Parents
www.adopting.org

www.rainbowkids.com

www.comeunity.com

www.karensadoptionlinks.com/

Resource Organizations for Adoptive Parents
http://naic.acf.hhs.gov/   National Adoption Information Clearinghouse

www.adoptioninstitute.org   The Evan B. Donaldson Adoption Institute

www.resolve.org   RESOLVE services on infertility and adoption

E-Mail Support Groups and Adoption Listservs
www.adopting.com/mailing.html A current list of all mailing lists, newsgroups and bulletin boards for various countries

Cultural and Travel Preparation Sites for Adoptive Parents
www.adoptiontravel.com includes a little bit of everything: books illustrating your child's birth country, medical information for your child's first check-up, and hints on travel.

www.eeadopt.net gives insights on the importance of carrying out your child's cultural heritage and offers resources for parents adopting from Eastern Europe.

www.ichild.org offers resources for parents adopting from India.

www.lapa.com offers resources for parents adopting from Latin America.

www.fwcc.org offers resources for parents adopting from China.

Resources for Dealing with the Issues of Adopted Children

www.comeunity.com provides information for adoptive families with children who have disabilities and special needs.

www.pnpic.org hosts the site of the Parent Network For The Post-Institutionalized Child (PNPIC).

Medical Resources for Adoptive Parents

www.peds.umn.edu/iac is the site for the International Adoption Clinic at the University of Minnesota.

www.orphandoctor.com is the site of the International Adoption Medical Consultation Services.

www.aap.org is the site for the American Academy of Pediatrics.

www.aafp.org is the site of the American Academy of Family Physicians.

www.immunize.org is the Immunization Action Coalition.

On-Line Magazines for Adoptive Parents

www.rainbowkids.com

http://magazines.adoption.com

A Final Word

We hope that, as you have worked through this workbook and added resources in this final chapter, this will serve as a wonderful tool for you as you begin parenting your newly-adopted child. Ideally, we suggest that much of this preparation and exploration occurs before your child's placement. But once your child is here, having a place where you have detailed information on available resources will be very helpful to you.

Our mission includes dedication to preparing parents for the life-changing experience of adoption.

We applaud you as you tackle the hard questions and seek out answers that might not be available from books.

Together we can make a difference in the lives of children.

With Eyes Wide Open available on CD

The CD format contains slide shows of children of various countries, short video and audio quips, and allows you to print out booklets and charts, do the homework sessions on your computer and e-mail them to a mentor, friend, or social worker. We invite you to try both styles of learning.

An order form for the workbook and CD is available on our web site,

www.childrenshomeadopt.org, where you will find current information and resources.

Since 1889, Children's Home Society & Family Services (CHSFS) has met the needs of children and families through our adoption, child abuse and neglect prevention, early childhood education and comprehensive family services. As a statewide non-profit 501 (c) (3) organization, CHSFS is committed to help children and families thrive. CHSFS touches the lives of over 33,000 individuals each year.

It is the mission of CHSFS to help children thrive and to build, strengthen and sustain individual, family and community life.

For more information, please visit the Children's Home Society & Family Services website, www.chsfs.org, or call 651-646-6393.